MW00994646

What early readers are saying about  *Happy*
SCHOOL

"This is my NEW MANUAL for living! Goodness, it's the Hallmark Channel meets Self Help." *Vicki L.*

"The wisdom and insight from *Happy School* is life-changing....As I read this book now, all I want to do is cheer, 'Thank you! Thank you!'" *Nancy G.*

"I love the story, love the principles, and love the way it is written! Every one of her books is awesome, but this might be the BEST!" *Leslie J.*

"How I loved reading this book! It is pure gold!...These principles of changing our thinking changes our very lives." *Sheri H.*

"The principles in *Happy School* have set me on a life-changing course....I cannot say enough positive things about this book—it will encourage everyone who struggles with 'glass-half-empty' tendencies." *Bethany S.*

"You are going to help so many women with this book, only eternity will tell!" *Denise H.*

"This book proves changing your thinking changes your life." *Kendall T.*

"I am encouraged by this book...to choose to live a happy life, no matter my circumstances or past. The principles in this book are so profound and yet so simple." *Jeanne N.*

"*Happy School* was a breath of fresh air....I'm so thankful for the light and truth within these pages, and for the first time in a while, I feel like I can fight for freedom within my mind." *Chelsea B.*

What readers have said about other books
in Julie Gordon's Genie Series

Wife
SCHOOL and *Skinny* SCHOOL

"Just finished reading your book. Love love love it! I especially love the way that it's written in fictional form. Awesome idea!" *Kerri G.*

"I just finished your book, and I LOVED it. I am recommending it to all of my friends." *Meredith G.*

"I plan to encourage all of the women I know to read this book." *Rebecca P.*

"I keep ordering more copies. You won't know until heaven how many lives may be changed through you." *Kim M.*

"WIVES...do not miss!! Many of my friends are raving over Julie Gordon's book(s)." *Chyrll V.*

"You cannot imagine how much of a 'God-breath' this book is to me." *Amy M.*

"I laughed out loud....I am buying this for our daughters....Wish I had had it years ago!" *Judy F.*

"My daughter gave me a copy of your book for Christmas, and I read it in two days. I could not put it down. I bought several copies and sent them to people." *Sondra S.*

"I tried to make (the *Genie* book) last as long as possible because I did not want it to end! It was absolutely amazing....It will definitely be permanently placed in my night stand....Can't wait for your next book!" *Heather J.*

"When I first read your book, my world was rocked. I am now guiding a small group of women through your amazing book!" *Elizabeth L.*

"A friend told me it was the best book she had read lately, so I read it over the summer. She was correct." *Anne F.*

"I promise you, I have had girls (that I mentor) come back and say this book has changed their lives forever. I have ordered twelve more copies and am mailing them to my closest friends." *Debbie F.*

"Wish I would've read this eleven years ago. Best BOOK I have ever, ever read!" *Cherisse H.*

"Please allow me to say that when something touches you the way your book has me, it takes no effort at all to show appreciation! Your book has shed so much light on every aspect of my life....I could not stop reading!" *Tynesha K.*

"I wish I had Julie Gordon's (books) to follow at the beginning of my marriage: life-changing." *Cate C.*

"Your book truly has been life-changing for me! I cannot thank you enough for writing this book." *Stephanie P.*

"Your book has helped me so much....Honestly, you have no idea. I have read AA books, co-dependency books, gone to AA meetings, church services, and so on...but nothing got the pieces in the slots and the gear oiled and turning the way your book did. I feel alive for the first time in eight years...in EIGHT YEARS!" *Kristin M.*

"(My newest daughter-in-law) thanked me in all capital letters for giving (your book) to her! She began reading it and can't put it down! She said she loves it!" *Carol F.*

"Thank you for your book! It has truly changed me." *Stacy R.*

"I am so thankful for your book and online study. It has literally revolutionized me and is teaching me what my heart was longing for but just didn't know how or where to go to learn these Godly truths." *Jill G.*

"Your guidance and knowledge are a God-send to me." *Kim B.*

"What a priceless gift I have through your book." *Erica V.*

"It has been an amazing gift, and it's unlike anything else I have read." *Jessica B.*

SCHOOL

WHERE WOMEN LEARN THE SECRETS
TO OVERCOME DISCOURAGEMENT & WORRY

Julie N. Gordon

Copyright © 2020 Julie N. Gordon

All rights reserved. This book or any portion thereof may not be reproduced or used in any manner whatsoever without the express written permission of the publisher except for the use of brief quotations in a book review.

ISBN: 978-0-578-73995-3 (paperback)

Cover design by Sonu Pawan.

Printed in the United States of America.

*Happy School: Where Women Learn the Secrets
to Overcome Discouragement and Worry*
is Book Three in the *Genie School* series for women.

BOOK ONE

Wife School: Where Women Learn the Secrets of Making Husbands Happy

BOOK TWO

Skinny School: Where Women Learn the Secrets to Finally Get Thin Forever

---

Also in the *Genie Series* with coauthor David Gordon

Husband School: Where Men Learn the Secrets of Making Wives Happy

Serve the LORD *with gladness.*

—Psalm 100:2 (NKJV)

Though the fig tree does not bud
and there are no grapes on the vines,
though the olive crop fails
and the fields produce no food,
though there are no sheep in the pen
and no cattle in the stalls,
yet I will rejoice in the Lord,
I will be joyful in God my Savior.

—Habakkuk 3:17–18 (NIV)

Dear Reader,

Theologians and philosophers have studied happiness for centuries, and the secrets are still the same as they were 6,000 years ago. There is truly *nothing new under the sun.*

To get the most out of this book, grab a few friends, read a chapter a week, and study the corresponding week/lesson in the *Happy School Study Guide* (available on Amazon). This book is a *course*, so be sure to do all the assignments in your own Quartz Journal (any notebook will do). Iron sharpens iron, and much mastery is gained when these lessons are studied and discussed with others.

If you've read any of my other books, you'll know that just as *Charlotte's Web*, *Chronicles of Narnia*, and the *Velveteen Rabbit* use animals and toys as their Wisdom characters, this book uses a Genie.

Freedom from heavy discouragement is right around the river bend.

In Jesus' service and for His kingdom,

Julie N. Gordon
July 7, 2020

Table of Contents

The Genie Arrives

Tuesday, August 21

On my lunch break, I hurriedly load sacks of groceries into the trunk of my car. I need to put the cold items in my fridge and be back at work in eighteen minutes. Once again, I realize I'm annoyed that Leland, my boyfriend, expects me to cook most nights. Although he does pay for the groceries—and honestly, I do love cooking—it still annoys me that he doesn't take me out more. Why, he can certainly afford it. Maybe during Leland's residency years he was understandably on a tight budget, but now, he's a board-certified ophthalmologist. After we get married, I'm sure Leland will learn to loosen his purse strings.

On the way to my apartment, I get a text from Leland. He knows I'm on my lunch break, so he wants me to run by his apartment and grab his long-sleeved, gray T-shirt. The text ends with, "Could you drop it off at my office? The temperature in this place is freezing."

Reading Leland's text sends another pang of irritation across my mind. Because Leland is a busy and *important* doctor, he assumes that I should not only be the one responsible for dinner but the one who uses her lunch break to run his errands. I agree that he works hard, but I am annoyed over this unspoken pattern of my being available at his beck and call. I mean, he doesn't support me, and I work, too (well, part-time).

After we're married, I hope he'll be more considerate of my time. His apartment is close by, and if I hurry, I'll only be five minutes late getting back from my lunch break. I text him that I'm on my way.

Leland works many nights until 7:00 p.m. I know that's a long day, so I understand that weekdays must have a no-frills feel. But on the weekends, he's so exhausted that all he wants to do is sleep, work out, drink a couple beers, and watch old movies.

Last Saturday night when we were at his apartment watching yet another rerun of one of the *Bourne Identity* movies, he fell asleep on the sofa after having a few beers. I was actually disgusted at the moment. I was struck by the thought that I'm bored out of my mind watching reruns every weekend. In this relationship, I've forfeited the emotional intimacy and romance I've always craved because Leland checks off some essentials that I want in a spouse: good (great) provider, intelligent, and good looking. Honestly, I'm not exceptionally happy in this relationship, but gosh, I can't be playing the field at thirty-two. This may not be ideal, but it's probably my last chance.

I've made a decision to give up fireworks in this relationship because I want children, and my fertility clock is ticking at an alarming rate. Don't all women who are approaching their mid-thirties—women who are ancient like me—have to give up on true love and settle? At least with Leland's income, I won't have to work, and I will have a beautiful house. I think having babies and a beautiful house will make me happy—because I'm certainly not happy now.

A wave of heaviness and deep sadness begins to descend. Marrying for love has always been something I've wanted but could never quite seem to figure out. Yes, there have been past relationships, but they always ended for some reason. I must be very broken and damaged. Here I am at thirty-two, getting ready to settle and marry for security. I'm pathetic. Just pathetic. But it doesn't seem like I have any other choice. I come from a damaged family, and now I'm damaged. As much as I try to cover up my inner angst in front of everyone else, I know deep down how messed up I am.

On top of Leland being inconsiderate and a royal bore, there is another problem: his mother. Leland once took me to visit his parents, who are farmers in East Tennessee. When I was alone with his mother in the kitchen after lunch, she asked me, "Is that a designer purse, Darby?"

"Yes," I said, waiting for her congratulatory remarks. "It's a Brahmin."

"Oh my!" she replied, shaking her head. "Why would anyone ever want to spend that kind of money on a purse?"

At once I understood that in her house, money was to be spent on land and fancy farm machinery, not on status items. I love fashion, and that's not going to change. But not wanting to rock the boat, I replied, "Brahmin purses are so durable that they last as long as three regular purses." That still did not impress her. I made a note that on my next visit I would leave my designer items at home.

I felt pretty certain that the weekend had gone poorly, but Leland assured me that everything was fine and that his parents were just old-fashioned and country. I remember thinking I was glad Leland and I would live in Memphis when we got married, which is seven hours from the farm.

About a year ago, I asked Leland if he ever thought about us getting married. He said of course he thought about it, but he wanted to first get established in his career. We've been dating two years next month, so I'm expecting a proposal any day. I might even hint about it again soon. After all, it will soon be time for me to get pregnant. Having several children—four to be exact—is something I've always wanted. So I need to get started.

Uh oh. My mother is calling. That's never a fun phone call. I don't answer, but she calls again. After the third try, she leaves a voicemail: "Darby, my college roommate, Gail, is coming to town this weekend, and I'm counting on you to make time this Saturday to have lunch with us. I know she'll want to see you."

Ugh! My mother always imposes her agenda on me. Gail could care less if she sees me or not. My mother is merely trying to fill her weekend. Since she views singles as having no real life of their own, she always feels she can impose her schedule on me. She would never ask my younger sister, Bailey—who is appropriately married with two little girls—to give up her Saturday afternoon to help her entertain an old friend. I wonder what excuse I can find to get out of this.

My mother still treats me like I'm thirteen, giving me repeated, unsolicited advice and direction. Just last week she said this:

> Why are you wearing red lipstick, Darby? That doesn't look good with your complexion. And it makes you look like you're trying too hard. I guess being thirty-two and single, though, you do have to try hard.

> Why aren't you and Leland engaged? Do you think he's going to break up? Is he just using you during his early medical career before he dumps you and marries someone else?

> Darby, my hips were not as big as yours when I was your age, even though I had had a baby.

(Just to be clear, my hips are *not* big, only curvy. They just don't fit my mother's ideal of an anorexic waif.)

Not surprisingly, I saw my first therapist when I was only eighteen. (Our family physician recommended an appointment because I broke down and cried during a routine annual visit, and I couldn't explain why.) On my first meeting with the therapist, I told him that I came from a perfect family. The therapist, who was seated behind a massive mahogany desk, asked me what I meant by "perfect."

"Well, we are all very good-looking and intelligent and have outgoing personalities," I explained.

I remember being shocked at the therapist's reply. "Young lady, you are very mixed up. Your mother controls and criticizes you, your parents have a hateful marriage, and you are an extremely unhappy and depressed young girl. Your family is anything but perfect."

It was as if I'd been living my life with my eyes half shut, and then a light came on. Immediately, I began to open up to the truth of how dysfunctional my family of origin truly was. Our unwritten family motto was twofold: "Protect family secrets, and impress others."

While I was growing up, my mother saw to it that my father and I were never close. If he was going to spend his life playing duplicate bridge, writing music, and cheating on her, then she would deny him a relationship with his oldest daughter. Of course, my little sister, Bailey, was shielded from all this family grime and even sat on Daddy's lap.

When I was in high school, my mother often let me skip school, writing bogus notes that said I wasn't feeling well, and then we would hang out at home together. I saw my mother as a victim of my selfish father's treatment, and I was determined to help her. We spent many hours together, and I became my mother's best friend and confidant, listening to her rage about how despicable a person my father was.

Because my dad was a songwriter, he barely made enough for us to scrape by. Even now in my mind, I can hear my mother screaming at him as he calmly walked out the door, all dressed up, to go play duplicate bridge. When my mother was fifty-five, she said she'd had enough and divorced my father.

After the divorce and after I became a Christian in college, I decided that I needed to develop a relationship with my dad. He responded well to the idea and started calling me and volunteering to help me with my projects such as hanging pictures at my apartment or getting the oil changed in my car.

One Saturday when I was doing laundry at my apartment, my mother arrived, unannounced. She stormed in and demanded that I quit pursuing a relationship with my dad. "I never left your father until you were grown so you would have a stable home in which to grow up. I did all of that for you, and now you betray me by trying to grow a relationship with him." She picked up some magazines on a coffee table and threw them on the floor.

Starting to shake, I told her that I wanted to have a relationship with him.

"What about me? What about all I've done for you?" she hurled. "How dare you betray me! I wish now that I had only looked out for myself and not stayed married as long as I did." She stormed out of the apartment, slamming the door.

In my little apartment kitchen, I remember watching my body shake. Looking back now, I know it was a panic attack. My mother, who always controlled me like a puppet, was pulling my strings again. Since I couldn't handle her ongoing wrath, I ended up doing as she requested and pulled back from my dad. My dad and I resumed pleasant conversations at holiday meals, but there was no real understanding between us. Of course, my mother never apologized (for this incident or any other) or even brought up the incident again. She just called me as she usually did and talked about her weight, her lack of money, and her clothes.

A few months after the divorce, Daddy wrote some amazing lyrics and music and sold three songs to some famous artists for top dollar. All three songs became hits. He made some pretty hefty money from this, for sure. But since it was after the divorce, my mother didn't get to enjoy any of it. She was furious! And then when Daddy died three years ago from a sudden heart attack, all that money went to Bailey and me. My mother tells me too often that we got *her* money.

Whenever I think about my family of origin, I begin to feel sorry for myself. It's no wonder I'm a basket case and have so many emotional issues. Even though I am now a Christian, I'll never heal from my broken launching pad. I'm screwed for life.

Getting Leland's T-shirt and dropping it off at his office takes a little longer than I calculated—fifteen extra minutes to be exact. As I walk back into my office building, Jana, my boss, is standing in the foyer. "That was a very long lunch, Darby," she says dryly. It's like she pressed a button on my emotions. My anger rises as I think back about Jana asking me to come in early and stay late, even though I'm paid on salary. I try to decide how to accurately defend myself. While I'm thinking, she says, "This is why I ask you to work extra, because I know you take long lunches." Then she prances off.

I thought that working in a law office would be impressive. But working as this ogre's administrative assistant is taking a toll on my health. I meander to my desk to finish out the day, but I'm still seething inside. I tell myself that the day after Leland proposes, I'm going to quit this job. I might not even give two weeks' notice. Ha! That would serve her right. Thoughts of revenge don't calm me, but they do arouse me. The Jana-types in the world make things miserable for the rest of us.

Eventually, 3:00 p.m. arrives, and I drive home. Pulling into my apartment parking lot, I look up at the blue sky and notice the gorgeous, billowy clouds. Their beauty makes me even sadder as I think how unhappy I am with my life. I wonder if the other people nearby are happy. I have almost forgotten what it feels like to be happy.

Suddenly, I am struck by the unpleasant thought that I should quit drinking those two glasses of wine each night. I think they dehydrate me, and they might even further lower my mood. I know that two (three?) glasses of wine every night is too much, but it is an immediate antidote for my boredom and misery.[1]

Carrying my groceries up the stairs to my apartment, I take stock of my crummy life—a boyfriend who is slow to propose while my eggs are decaying, a heartless boss who thinks I exist merely as a robot to do her work, a mother who is crazy, a bad habit of drinking too much, and huge overall boredom and despair about life. I hate it. I'm soooo unhappy! I don't like my circumstances, yet I don't know how to fix things. Dark discouragement descends even more. It's almost as if a thick, dark cloud is pressing itself on my brain, and I'm helpless to get rid of it.

Then to make matters worse, I remember that my roommate, Shelby, is late again paying her half of the rent. She never has any money, so I often pay her half until she can scramble and come up with her portion later. This is the latest she's ever been, though. Rent is due on the 5th, and

---

1. Darby has several bad habits, including overspending and drinking too much. The Genie will address the topic of acquiring discipline to stop bad habits in Lesson 4. One of my prior books, *Skinny School: Where Women Learn the Secrets to Get Thin Forever*, deals extensively with learning the thinking patterns to overcome the bad habit of eating sugar and junk food. Therefore, that problem will not be specifically addressed in this book (although the principles to stop any bad habit are basically the same).

this is the 23rd. She is a hair stylist here in town, and she says her upscale studio rent eats up most of her profits.

As I approach my front door, I notice that there is a package outside my door. Picking it up, I carry it into my apartment. It's strange that there is no return address on the box.

When I open the package, I discover a mahogany box. I proceed to open this box, and inside is an old brass lamp with a handle and a spout. It looks like it belonged to Aladdin. Is this some kind of joke? Who would send me this junk?

Picking up the Aladdin-like lamp, I notice a cork in the spout. Maybe the gift-giver left a note inside the lantern. I remove the cork from the spout, and a pillar of smoke pours out. Naturally, I'm terrified. Dropping the lamp on the sofa, I run into the hallway to escape what I fear is going to be an explosion. But there is no explosion. I peek back around the corner.

Standing there in my den is a dark, middle-aged, Middle Eastern man. He is about six feet tall and looks like he has worked out every day of his life. His tan skin looks a little dry, like men who are sailors or who have played tennis without sunscreen all their lives. His eyebrows are a little on the bushy side, but they make his face interesting. His gaze is his most surprising feature—soft and filled with kindness, free of any malice. Gold silk pants are topped off with a white vest embroidered with gold thread and a large turban populated with sparkling gems on his head.

He sees me and motions for me to come to him. "Do not be afraid. I am your Genie, and I am here to grant you one wish."

Who is this criminal? Is this a dream? I slap my thigh, but I don't think I wake up.

"It's true," he continues. **"I am your genie, and I'm here to grant you one wish, Young Darby. What is your wish?"**

How does he know my name? Who is this? My heart rate must be 200, but his calm eyes tell me that I'm safe. I slowly move toward him.

"Go ahead. Tell me your wish, Young Darby."

After ten more minutes of this repetitive dialogue where I question him, touch him, and slap myself again to wake up, I realize that if this is a dream, I will eventually wake up, so I might as well go along with his instructions.

"Okay, Genie, my one wish is this: I want to be happy."

"Your wish is my command, Young Darby. Would you like to begin the lessons now?"

"Wa…wa…wait a second. Begin wh…wh…what lessons?" I ask. "Can't you just say 'abracadabra' and make me happy?"

"Of course I can," he says. "But you would still have the same thoughts, attitudes, and behaviors, and in a matter of weeks, you'd be right back where you are today. No, I'm not going to do a short-term fix. I am going to enroll you in my course, *Happy School*. The art and science of happiness is not new. Philosophers and theologians have studied happiness for centuries. In addition, psychologists and social scientists are now scientifically studying and documenting the subject. I will teach you the secrets, and then you can become staggeringly happier. Happiness is actually a learnable skill."

Uh, right. This cartoon creature has answers I haven't found on *YouTube* or in the scores of books I've read.

"Humans have searched for happiness for centuries," he says, "and now we know there are actual thought processes and actions that chronically disappointed and discouraged people repeatedly think and do. Likewise, there is a habitual way of thinking and acting that positive, optimistic, and happy people engage in. The path has been discovered, documented, mapped, and categorized.[2] I am going to teach you how to recognize thoughts and actions that cause unhappiness and then teach you the thoughts and actions that cause happiness. You can retrain your brain to actually think differently."

"Wait a minute," I say. "I'm not unhappy because of my thinking or acting. I'm unhappy because of my terrible circumstances and because I

---

2. This is not to downplay the suffering and tragedy that take place in life. However, it is true that even in the most despicable circumstances such as the Holocaust, some people still chose to live with meaning and purpose and went about sharing their bread (from *Man's Search for Meaning* by Victor Frankl).

have bad brain chemistry. If I had a wonderful husband, a sane mother, and good brain chemicals, I'd be happy."

"Not so fast, Young Darby. That is not necessarily true.[3] Be patient, and I will explain it all to you. Actually, overcoming chronic discouragement and developing a happy heart are both learnable skills, Young Darby. You can rewire your neural pathways and teach yourself to think differently. This is a curriculum, much like learning to play chess or learning to play the piano. After I teach you the ten principles, you must practice the tenets to achieve mastery."

How stupid is this? A course to become happy? What I need is for my mother to move to the Florida Keys where there is no cell phone reception.

"All problems in your life will never go away," he says. "But you can learn to think correctly about the obstacles in your life and about what is missing and disappointing. You do not need to *invent* rules for thinking about your problems; you only need to *discover* the correct ones and replace your current thinking patterns with them."

"My thinking patterns are fine," I respond. "It's my circumstances that are janked up." I already said that. Doesn't he listen?

"Actually, circumstances only minimally determine your happiness. It's your thinking patterns that overwhelmingly determine your happiness," he says.

What a ridiculous statement. Everyone knows circumstances determine your happiness.

"When the Creator created humans," he continues, "He created laws and rules for correct thinking patterns that correlate to mental health, even in the midst of trials. If His rules are violated (similar to violating rules for physical health), the Creator's image-bearers will suffer discouragement and depression."

I'm sure his analogy is incorrect.

---

3. Of course, there is some true mental illness. But the vast majority of people who are depressed have wrong thinking habits, and *that is what has caused the chemical imbalance.* It is true that some medications, metal toxicity, and illnesses also produce depression.

"People learn how to think differently all the time by renewing their minds," he says.[4] "The mind is very plastic, which means it can change. You now have many deeply carved neural pathways in your brain, much like schoolyard paths. But just as if a new schoolyard path is opened and repeatedly walked on (and the first path is no longer used), the second path becomes stronger and more defined while the first path gets weaker. Your neural pathways are similar. We are going to extinguish thought and behavior patterns that cause discouragement and add new thought and behavior patterns that produce joy."

I'm too damaged for this.

"There are many lessons in *Happy School* for you to learn, so you will need a journal to collect your notes and thoughts." He twirls his hand in the air, and a beautiful, quartz-colored journal adorned with various gems appears. "We will collect all our lessons in this Quartz Journal."[5]

I wonder if these are fake gems or the real thing.

"You have a habit of thinking disappointing and discouraging thoughts. I will teach you how to rebuild your mind so you are happy."

I think disappointing and discouraging thoughts because my life is disappointing and discouraging. How does he propose to change that?

"Similar to learning to play chess or the piano, I can teach you the very basics in two weeks," he says. "But to acquire mastery, it is up to you to do the work to rewire your thinking. If you follow my instructions, you will not even recognize your internal mental landscape in five years."

"Five years?" I gasp. "I can't wait five years."

"It takes five years to develop mastery in any field," he explains. "You will immediately begin to improve your happiness level, but again, like playing chess or the piano, you must put in the practice to acquire mastery."

I decide to say what I'm thinking. "Genie, this may work for some people, but I've had emotional disturbance since I was a teen."

---

4. Romans 12:1–2
5. All the exercises for your Quartz Journal are located in the back of this book.

"Although you may not become the most rosy, optimistic person in the world, you can hugely, magnificently, and monumentally change the landscape of your brain and become a reliably positive and happy person," he promises.

"I'm exhausted from trying so many things to find happiness," I say. "I've tried counseling, medication, essential oils, yoga, and many other healing modalities. Nothing has worked." I am seriously skeptical of his claims.

"My teachings are not my own ideas," he says, "but the accumulation of the sage wisdom of the centuries. These principles transform the mind. I'm off to Burma for a special sale on sandals. But I'll return soon for our first lesson." He twirls into a spiral funnel of air and disappears.

This is stupid, and I slap myself again to try to awaken from this dumb dream. I have zero energy to learn some idiotic lessons. As I said, I'm exhausted from trying to overcome my chronic disappointment with life. Actually, I feel rather hopeless.[6]

Glancing at the clock, I realize I need to hurry so I can be at Leland's by 6:00 p.m. to start dinner.

Leland and I simultaneously arrive at his apartment. Tonight I'm cooking chicken breasts with za'atar spices topped with a lemon almond-tahini sauce. While I begin cooking, Leland proceeds to talk nonstop about the new retirement plan his office just announced, how *non*-generous it is, and that since he's the new guy, he can't complain.

I thought I might bring up getting engaged tonight, but I can sense it is clearly not the time as he is *not* in a good mood. His energy is like a broken doorknob. His energy instantly escalates, however, as he reads a text message. He begins laughing hysterically at it.

"What's that?" I ask, noticing his abrupt change of mood.

6. Darby is severely discouraged, even depressed. But she is not suicidal. If you have thoughts of suicide, please reach out for help. *Happy School* can greatly help you with your thinking and your depression, but you may need some medical intervention in the meantime until you can learn and practice all the tenets. Do not give in to despair. Things can change 100 percent. With God, all things are possible.

"It's from Bethany. It's about a funny thing that happened at work today. It would take too long to explain the context, and it's not important," he says, letting me know he doesn't want to talk about it further.

The fact that he has a private joke going on with my (supposed) friend and his co-worker, Bethany and doesn't want to tell me about it is insulting.

Bethany was a sorority sister of mine in college. The old sorority friend group still meets once a month for dinner. Everyone in the group is married with kids except Bethany and, of course, pathetic me. Six months ago at a group dinner, Bethany told me she had undergone special training and received certification as an ophthalmic assistant and was looking for a job. She knew my boyfriend was an ophthalmologist, so she asked me to put in a good word for her with Leland since she was applying at his clinic. Well, Leland's ophthalmic group hired her. Honestly, I've never liked or trusted Bethany.

A few weeks ago when I asked Leland how Bethany was working out, he said, "Really well. Man, she's built!" I was offended, and I was also offended back in college when Bethany used to talk openly about *her own breasts*. She called them "The Girls." I mean, it was her identity, and I found it disgusting. Then as well as now, I feel like Bethany is dull and dim-witted. The fact that she and Leland are now big buddies feels disrespectful. I guess since they work together, she has the freedom to text him as friends, but still.

After dinner, Leland searches for a movie for us to watch. I'm still simmering over Bethany's text, but I decide to bring up the engagement issue anyway. When I look over at Leland, he is asleep. Frustrated, I let myself out and drive home, thinking how much I hate his private jokes with Bethany, how much I hate his watching so much TV, how much I hate how he doesn't take me out more, and how much I hate that he hasn't proposed. Again, I think having some adorable babies and a gorgeous house will make me happy. I will bring up our engagement earlier in the evening tomorrow. Surely he's been thinking about it.

When I get home, I pour myself a second glass of wine and settle down to do a little online shopping. I usually don't have more than two—at the most three—glasses (not counting a couple weddings I've been to), so surely this is not too much.

Today I saw some Tory Burch pumps on another woman. I'd like to order them for myself. I type the description into the search bar on the Tory Burch website and find them. Oh, they are $378. Well, I have so few pleasures in life, and nice fashion is definitely one of them. I fill out the form and click *Order*. I can always send them back if I don't love them. I will need them for my honeymoon since I want to go to London. The sightseeing, shows, and restaurants will entertain me since Leland doesn't.

Grabbing my new copy of *Architectural Digest*, I salivate over the gorgeous room designs. As soon as Leland and I get married, I will start working on him to buy a house that I can make into a showplace. Marble floors, high ceilings, and open, spacious rooms are lovely to behold. Leland's mother didn't like my designer purses. Just wait until she sees my designer house.

My misery has temporarily dwindled. Drinking, reading design magazines, and shopping online are triplet analgesic activities that temporarily soothe me. But of course, the twin cousins of despair and discouragement will return tomorrow, as they always do. My life is so pathetic that nothing could change things, especially the Genie's little secrets to overcoming discouragement and worry.

After changing into my pajamas, I receive several text messages in a row. My mother is texting me again about meeting with her and her friend Gail on Saturday. My sister, Bailey, wants me to babysit next weekend so she and her husband can have a date night. But oh! Here's a good text. My friend Ellie wants me to attend the Vesta Home Show with her on Saturday. Ah, the perfect excuse to give my mother for declining her lunch invitation. Ellie's text is the only one I return.

Hearing the front door open, I know that Shelby, my roommate, is home. I should probably confront the past due rent money, but I'm too wiped out. My door is shut, and she never bothers me when my door is shut.

On my desk is a pile of bills. I open them—American Express, MasterCard, Visa, Zara, Nordstrom, and Anthropologie. Leland would die if he knew how much I spend on clothes. Using my inheritance from my dad, I consider paying the minimum on each bill, but I decide to do it later. I quickly tally up the balances, and the total is over $5,000. Leland will not like paying these off when we get married, but with his colossal salary, he can easily do it. I won't say anything until after the wedding. Really, in the scheme of an ophthalmologist's salary, this is small change.

I walk into my bathroom to get floss and glance in the mirror. My skin is fair and clear, although a tiny bit freckled just like my dad's Scottish relatives. My red hair has a wee bit of blonde, so that allows me to claim that my hair color is strawberry blonde. I mostly like my coloring except that my emotions make me blush easily. Since I have very light eyelashes and eyebrows, it's imperative that I wear makeup.

One time when Leland saw me without makeup, he asked, "So this is how you look without makeup? Can't you buy permanent makeup?" I thought it was mean.

My cheekbones are high, but I'm definitely not beautiful by any sense of the word. But with all the makeup available now for women, I can look nice if I try hard.

And although I'm not naturally muscular, I work out a lot, so I have acquired a little definition. Recently, my mother saw me in shorts and said, "I never thought your ugly legs would look decent. Who would think that exercise could change legs so much?" Somehow even her compliments are critical.

Again, I realize how everything stinks in my life. I begin to mentally list my many circumstances that are heavy and unwanted—Leland not proposing, Leland having secret jokes with Bethany, my mother's jabs, my crummy job, my slow-paying roommate.

Before leaving the bathroom, I notice some wrinkles I had not noticed before. Oh, no! Not only are my eggs decaying at supersonic speed but I'm *wrinkling*. How I hate it all.

Sometimes I feel guilty because I know I should be helping others more and making more of a contribution to society. When I see a needy person, my heart does go out to them, and I think how I could help. For example, I have often thought about volunteering for a pro-life organization because I am so passionately opposed to abortion. And there's a tutoring program here in town for underprivileged children that I have often considered signing up for.

But then I remember how many of my own personal trials I must deal with, and I know I can't take on someone else's struggles just yet. Guilt reminds me that I'm not a good person, and that makes me feel doubly terrible. I spend too much. I drink too much. I'm too angry. I'm just a total 100 percent unhappy mess. I'd like to change, but I have absolutely no idea how to fix my small issues, much less my huge ones.

Goodnight, world. Ugh! I hate my life. I hate it all.[7]

(A summary and review of the Genie's teachings
can be found at the back of this book.)

---

7. *I again would like to repeat this important warning:* Darby is severely discouraged, perhaps depressed. But she is not suicidal. If you have thoughts of suicide, you must tell someone who can help, such as a counselor or a pastor. Reach out to someone who can help right this minute if you have any thought of taking your own life.

Lesson 1

Thinking Determines Emotions and The Magic of Moving into Another Room in Your Brain

Wednesday, August 22

It's five minutes before 3:00, which is quitting time. My boss, Jana, walks up to my desk and says, "Darby, I need you to drop these documents off at the Smith and Tyler Law Firm before you go home today."

"Actually, I've got to leave right at 3:00 today," I say. I don't say why because she may not think my reasons are valid. But they're important to me. I'm going to go shopping for special food and take extra time to look good because tonight I'm going to talk to Leland about our engagement.

"Oh, you've got a doctor's appointment?" Jana asks. It's uncomfortable, especially after that confrontation yesterday.

"No, I've got an important night tonight and lots to do to prepare for it," I say.

She frowns, and I know she doesn't like my answer. "The Smith firm is less than fifteen minutes from here," she says, pressing me.

I need this job until I'm engaged, so as always, I comply. "Well, I'm short on time," I say, "but maybe if I hurry, I can do it." Before I can change my mind, she jams a large, sealed envelope into my hands.

"Thanks," she mutters as she briskly walks away without even looking at me.

With traffic, Jana's errand takes almost forty-five minutes, so now I have to hurry home to get the prep work done for dinner. I am truly going the extra mile tonight. I am making beef kabobs seasoned with a tangy spice blend and a creole mayonnaise sauce on the side. I have a slew of faults, but there are two things I seem to be okay at doing (well, actually pretty good at doing)—cooking and interior design.

Leland loved the meal, as I knew he would. After cleaning up the mess, I cozily join him on the sofa where he is scrolling through the options of what we can watch on TV tonight.

"Leland," I say in a very sweet voice, "you said that after you were established in your career that maybe we could talk about getting engaged. Are you established yet?"

He and I both know he is since he's been working this job with great success for the last nine months. He turns to look at me. I spent extra time on my makeup and hair tonight so I feel confident about how I look. Although my mother makes me cringe in many ways, she did bequeath me high cheekbones and clear skin.

"There's something you should know, Darby," he says slowly, looking down, searching for words. "If we get married, it's against my mother's wishes."

Although I'm not completely surprised to hear this, I am still upset by it. I wait to hear more.

"My mother says you'll spend every dime I make and then some," he continues.

Maybe the spending statement has a hair of truth to it, but he's going to make plenty of money, so he can afford to buy me a gorgeous house and some designer clothes. My heart rate speeds to a thunderous beat that I think I can hear.

"Why haven't you told me this?" I ask, appearing calm but sensing a tornado brewing inside.

"I don't know, Darby. I've been swamped with school and then work, and I didn't want to rock the boat," he replies, looking away from me as he finishes.

"How could you ever go against your mother's wishes and marry someone when she's not supportive?" I ask. Now is his opportunity to tell me that I'm worth it, I'm the love of his life, I'm the only one, and so on.

"To be honest, I can't figure that out," he says, still looking away.

Surely there is something else he is going to say. I wait, but he doesn't say a word. It starts to sink in. *He has already decided he's not going to marry me.*

"So you've known we weren't going to get married, but you didn't want to rock the boat because you needed a girlfriend?" I ask, somewhat rhetorically.

"It's not like I thought it through," he says, now with his face down.

This coward is telling me that he's just wasted two years of my life, knowing he was not going to marry me, basically admitting he was using me.

Continuing to remain calm on the outside but feeling inside that wild stallions have been released to stampede, I ask, "You knew the whole time that you weren't going to marry me, but you dated me anyhow?"

I'm waiting for him to disagree. But he doesn't. Finally looking at me, he says, "Like I said, I didn't carefully think it through. I'm sorry. I have been pressed against the wall for seven years with medical school and residency."

The Goliath-sized anger I am experiencing feels like it's getting ready to explode. This is the lowest, meanest, most selfish thing I've ever experienced. I'm about to unload full vent, but the thought that Leland and I share many mutual friends (and that he will tell them everything I say) comes to mind. I decide to not create any more fallout, so I make an outwardly noble move.

"Goodbye, Leland," I say, calmly getting up, gathering my dishes, and walking to the door.

"Where are you going?" he says, standing up and following me.

The comments I'd like to say—but, of course, don't—come flooding in:

You are the most pathetic form of a human being I've ever met. Scum, pure scum.

I hate you so much that I hope your life fails in every way. I hate you. And your mom.

I only stayed around because you're a handsome doctor, you bozo. You're really a terrible bore.

I'll never know where I got the frame of mind to silently leave without going into his kitchen and tossing all the glass dishes onto the floor.

Leland follows me as I march steadily to my car. Again, from somewhere, I have the discernment to act composed and, in fact, even regal. With calm confidence, I open my car door, get in, start the car, and without even one more word or one more look in his direction, drive away.

When I'm around the corner, I break down in uncontrollable sobs—not tears over losing Leland necessarily, but tears over being used for two important biological clock-ticking years! His mother! His judgmental, tightwad, despicable mother!

I have been bamboozled. I am stunned. I thought I was getting ready to marry a doctor, and now I'm single again at thirty-two. My phone rings before I get home. It's my mother. She is the *last* person on earth I want to talk to. I try to tap *decline* on my phone, but since my fingers are shaking, I accidentally tap *accept*. I consider just hanging up but then decide to go ahead and get this phone call over with.

"I'm super busy, Mom. Can I call you back?" I say, trying to conceal my teary voice. I put the phone on mute when I'm not talking.

"Sure," she says but then starts talking as though she didn't even hear me. "Forget about that lunch on Saturday. Something important has come up. My birthday is Friday, and Bailey is having everyone over to her house for dinner. Isn't that just the sweetest thing ever? She is so thoughtful. Anyhow, I want you and Leland to come."

"I can come," I say. And then against my better judgment, I add, "But Leland won't be there. We broke up."

"You and Leland *what*?" she gasps. "Oh, I knew it. I just knew it. I knew that relationship wasn't going well. I could tell the last time I saw you with him that he was losing interest. Oh, Darby! You're thirty-two! Almost thirty-three! This isn't good. This isn't good at all."

I hold my cell phone away from me and stare at it in disbelief.

"I've got an important call on the other line that I've got to take, Mom, so I'll call you back." I lied. Lying is not a sin when you have a mother like mine.

"Okay," she says, "but try to bring some normal food on Friday night. Please don't bring some off-the-wall gourmet thing."

"Okay, but I've got to go," I say, ignoring her critical remark and hanging up. I wonder to what other city I could move. I let myself sob out loud again and think about Atlanta or maybe Dallas. Maybe moving would help my sorry life.

Continuing my drive home, I try to process what just happened with Leland. Again, I realize I am not upset that I've lost some true love. It's because here I am again—single, hating my life, and seriously worrying that my mother is affecting my mental stability. I've got to fix something, but I don't know what or how.

Pulling into my parking lot, I notice I'm still shaking. I feel hopeless, empty, and completely dejected. Gathering my belongings, I get ready to open the car door.

"Good evening, Young Darby," a deep voice says.

I'm startled by the voice, but when I look over at the passenger seat, I see the Genie sitting there eating from a bowl.

"I wasn't finished eating my Babylonian sheep stew, but I knew I had to catch you before you went into your apartment," he says. He takes one last bite. "There, finished. Let's begin Lesson 1 in *Happy School*. This lesson has three parts and..."

"Genie, I've had a very hard night," I interrupt. "My boyfriend and I..."

"I know," he says before my sad story really gets going. "Therefore, this is an especially important time for you to learn how to overcome discouragement and worry. Here is your Quartz Journal so you can take notes."

Yes, discouragement, despair, depression, disappointment, unhappiness, and turmoil. I've got it all. Seeing that I am not going to dissuade him from continuing, I push my seat back and get ready to take notes.

"There are three extremely important foundational truths to grasp in Lesson 1," he begins.

Maybe this genie has helped some other people out of their unhappiness dungeons, but he won't be able to help me. I'm too deeply broken, and my life is absolutely abominable. There is no changing that.

"The first truth to understand in Lesson 1 is that all of your *emotions* are produced from your prior *thoughts*. If you are feeling sad, it is because you just had a sad thought. If you feel scared, it is because you just had a fearful thought. This is always true."

Wait a minute. Wait. One. Minute. It's not my thinking that is the problem. My sadness comes from my rotten childhood where I didn't get what I needed emotionally. And my current discouragement comes from my lousy circumstances. I don't explain this to the Genie yet. I decide to let him go on a little more before I correct him.

"Sometimes you might feel angry," he says, "and you do not even realize that you've just had a prior angry thought. It is important that you know that whenever you have *any* emotion, you can always back it up and see what *prior* thought you were thinking. If we could put your thoughts and subsequent emotions on a computer screen, you would see a perfect correlation."

"Are you sure this is right?" I ask, knowing it's not but still not wanting to challenge him this early in the course.

"Let me demonstrate by giving you a couple of examples," he says. "Imagine you are in a dark alley by yourself in one of the roughest parts of town at midnight. It is quiet until suddenly you hear a trash can tip over and see a cat dart across your path. What is your emotion?"

"Fear, of course," I say. This is stupid and obvious.

"You are correct," he says. "But follow this line of thinking. The truth of that situation is that no one is around for a mile. You are perfectly safe. So did your emotion of fear follow your thoughts (of possible danger), or did your emotion of fear come from reality (remember, reality was that you were safe because no one was within a mile)?"

"I don't understand," I say.

"Your emotion of fear came from your *thoughts about your situation, not reality*," he explains.

"I guess I follow that. Sort of."

"Let's try another scenario. Pretend you hear that a very attractive young man and one that you're interested in wants your phone number. What are your emotions?"

Playing along, I say, "Well, since I am destined to be an old maid, I'm sure that would be a welcome situation, and I'd be hopeful and excited."

"Hopeful and excited is exactly how you would feel," he says. "But then let's suppose you find out it was actually another girl named Darby whose phone number he wanted, not yours. Did your emotions of hopefulness and excitement follow your *thoughts* (thinking an attractive young man was interested in you), or did your emotions of hopefulness and excitement follow reality?"

"Uh, well, I guess my emotions followed my thoughts, not reality," I say, beginning to follow him a little bit. It seems like with my desperate situation, we should instead be talking about my deplorable circumstances, but I decide again to be polite.

"Your emotions of discouragement are from thinking discouraging, negative thoughts," he says. "I am now getting ready to give you some life-transforming sentences, and I want you to write them down in bold in your Quartz Journal."

Oh, dear. So dramatic.

"Ready?" he asks. "Here they are: Because your emotions come from prior thoughts, you are therefore not the *victim* of your emotions but the *producer* of them.[8] You have been producing your emotional climate by your own thoughts. You master your moods by mastering your thoughts."

Maybe this is true occasionally for some people, but my discouragement is from deep-seated, unchangeable genetic causes. I do, nevertheless, write the sentences in all caps in my Quartz Journal.

"That brings us to the second part of today's lesson," he says. "When the Creator made the human mind, He made it so it can only think *one thought* at a time."

Now I must interrupt and correct him. "Genie, I am the queen of multi-tasking. In fact, I excel at doing several things at the same time." I hope I don't have to keep correcting this Genie.

"Young Darby, what you are good at is switching back-and-forth between tasks very quickly. The human mind can only think one thought at a time."

I'll let it go. It doesn't seem like a hill to die on.

"The third part of today's lesson is that humans,[9] made in the image of the Creator, *have the power to watch the Parade of Thoughts that March across Their Brains.* The human brain has the phenomenal ability to 'think about its own thinking.' The scientific word for this is *metacognition*. Humans have the capacity to stand back from their thoughts and listen in on their own self-talk."

I'm hopelessly discouraged, and he's giving me a lesson on neurology?

"Not only can humans listen in on their self-talk," he continues, "but they can *interrupt* those thoughts. I call this Playing Hot Potatoes. One can choose to stop thinking a current thought by *intentionally thinking about something else* (since the human brain can only think one thought at a time). In *Happy School*, I call this *Moving into Another Room in Your Brain*, and it is one of the most life-changing skills you will ever learn."

---

8. This is one of the utmost key premises of this book: You are not the *victim* of your emotions but the *producer* of them.

9. Humans are made in the image of the Creator and can "think about their thinking." No animal can do this.

Whoa! I've got to stop him. "How could I ever possibly control what I think?" I blurt out, knowing that this would never be possible for me to do with all my terrible circumstances. "It seems like my consuming circumstances *insist* that I think about them constantly."

"When you realize that the Parade that Marches across Your Brain has a negative nature, you can interrupt those thoughts by Playing Hot Potatoes. You quickly kick the negative thought out by consciously choosing to think about *something else*; that is, by Moving into Another Room in Your Brain. It can be as simple as thinking about and making a grocery list or thinking about something as profound as what you are grateful for. But since you can only think one thought at a time, you can choose to think about something other than the original negative thought."

Now this is downright ridiculous. How would one ever decide *not* to think about a horrible situation such as Leland using me and then discarding me? Before I can object, the Genie continues.

"And since feelings follow thoughts, when you change thoughts, your feelings will follow," he says. "This is a life-changing process to learn as you discover that you have the power to cast off negative thoughts and thus *cast off negative emotions*. You can choose to insert (think about) whatever thoughts you choose."

Surely if this were true, I would have read about this online somewhere with all the time I spend on my phone.

"This skill gives you power over the emotional environment you live in since you can hear what thoughts you're thinking (the Parade that Marches across Your Brain), interrupt negative thoughts (Play Hot Potatoes), and then insert other thoughts instead (Moving into Another Room in Your Brain)."

Does he think I'm in kindergarten with all the cutesy names? Next he's going to tell me we're going to play the Quiet Game.

"Your discouragement and heavy heart are from thinking negative thoughts, and you have the power to exchange those thoughts for neutral—or even optimistic and hopeful—thoughts.

Optimistic is not a word I've ever used to describe myself.

"Learning to listen in on the Parade that Marches across Your Brain (your self-talk) and then subsequently interrupting and replacing the negative thoughts *will completely transform* the mental and emotional landscape in which you now live," he says. "You will go from being a person with chronic disappointment and discouragement to one who is repeatedly contented and happy."

I don't think he understands the depth of the emotional issues I'm dealing with.

"When you are feeling an unwanted emotion," he continues, "know that it will dissipate when you choose to think neutral or positive thoughts."

Surely this information would have been reported on my News Feed. I'll show him he's wrong since my discouragement is not from thinking wrong thoughts.

"I once had a doctor tell me I have a chemical imbalance," I offer as proof. So there! My discouragement is not my fault from thinking negative thoughts.

"You probably currently do have a chemical imbalance," he agrees. "Thoughts are actual 'things' and cause chemical reactions in your body. For example, you know that when you feel fear, your heart rate increases. Thinking and ruminating on negative thoughts have caused a chemical imbalance in your brain. But when you learn to *think positive, hopeful, and true thoughts,* your chemical imbalance will begin to heal."

True thoughts? The truth is that all the good men at thirty-two are gone, and I am destined to be alone and childless.

"As I said before, repeated thoughts, like children walking on a schoolyard path, carve deep grooves or neural pathways in your brain," the Genie continues. "But when you begin to think different thoughts, it is like you are forging a new path in your brain, and the old brain grooves will begin to heal."

All of his neuroscience nonsense is not going to alter my messed up life. "This sounds kind of New Age-y, Genie," I say in protest.

"New Age-y?" he says and laughs. "Actually, this is *ancient* thinking. These principles are how the Creator designed humans to think.[10] His plan was for His children to rejoice, have courage, feel blessed, have hope, learn trust, walk by faith, and find opportunity in obstacles and trials. The ten principles I'm going to teach you are all timeless, ancient principles."

He won't have a response to my next statement. "I didn't have the best childhood, Genie. I didn't get what I needed emotionally as a child, and I think my general sadness and melancholy are from that imperfect beginning."

"I cannot tell you how often people say that to me," he replies. "You may have learned some negative thinking patterns from those days, which we will address, but your current emotions are from your current thoughts. And now, as an adult, you can choose to completely reprogram your thoughts."[11]

I'm sure it's not as easy as he suggests.

"Your mind is a battleground, and you win the battle by intentionally choosing what you think about," he says.[12] "There are ten lessons in *Happy School*, and by the end of our course, you will completely comprehend what I'm trying to teach you. Just be patient."

How can I be patient with my eggs aging at the speed of light?

"Genie, I don't want to be some naïve ostrich with my head in the sand while my problems grow around me," I argue.

"Of course you need to face your problems," he agrees. "We will talk extensively about that subject in our next meeting when I present

---

10. While in the midst of the horrendous circumstances of a first-century Roman prison, the Apostle Paul wrote what to think about: whatever is pure, noble, right, pure, lovely, admirable, excellent, and praiseworthy (Philippians 4:8).

11. The Apostle Paul tells us to renew our minds (Romans 12:1–2).

12. In ancient times, men wore flowing robes. When they had work to do or had to move quickly, they secured or girded up their flowing robes in their belts. The Bible says to "gird up the loins of your mind" (1 Peter 1:13 NKJV). This teaching commands that we corral and control the thoughts in our minds instead of letting them run helter-skelter like hooligans. Humans are to think in a certain way.

Lesson 2, which is how to think correctly about What's Missing and Disappointing in your life (I call them WMDs)."

Everything is missing and disappointing in my life. I wonder how he proposes to fix that.

"From now on," he says, "I want your negative emotions to be like the warning lights on your car's dashboard, alerting you to pay attention to your prior thoughts. I am off to Persia for a magic carpet race, but I will return shortly," he says as he spins into a cyclone-shaped sphere and disappears.

As I sit alone in my car, I think about what the Genie claimed was a monumental sentence: I am not the *victim* of my emotions but the *producer* of them. It's a nice premise in theory, but I don't see how anyone with my atrocious life could have any response but severe discouragement. This first lesson certainly didn't help me with my dreadful existence.

After heading up the stairs to my apartment, I see that the apartment door is open. Inside is Shelby, my slow-paying roommate. She is in the kitchen taking dishes out of the cabinet, wrapping them in paper, and putting them in a box. I notice that she is painfully thin with mousy brown hair and stooped shoulders. "What are you doing?" I ask.

"Darby, I'm moving. My grandmother lives in Martha's Vineyard, and she said I can move in with her. I'm going to get a fresh start. I know I owe you some money, and I'll try to send it to you when I get to Nantucket and get a job."

"Uh, Shelby, you made a verbal agreement to live here with me for a year. My name is on the lease, so I'm going to be responsible for both our rents," I say, not believing that she would leave me on such short notice.

"I'm sorry," she says. "I know it's not ideal. Like I said, when I get settled, I'll send you some money…if I can."

If she can? I'll never see a single cent.

Shelby starts crying, a sign that I'm not supposed to bother her anymore. It's a manipulative ploy so I'll perceive her as hurt and needy and let her get by with this.

Leland warned me not to get involved with Shelby when she wouldn't sign the lease. I knew he was right, but I didn't listen. Now I'm stuck with her half of the rent. I feel my anger rising.

Shelby starts sobbing louder, so I walk to my room and shut the door. Gosh, I can be such an idiot. Why did I let her move in without signing the lease? I can't believe how dumb that was.

I check my phone to see if possibly I missed a text from Leland declaring the depth of his regret, his inconceivable mistake, and the horror he feels at the possibility of living without me.

Not a word.

The sorrow of my life again washes over me. Leland used me, his ghastly mother influenced him against me, my harebrained mother torments me, my sister and my roommate mistreat me, my heinous boss abuses me, and my eggs and face almost qualify me for being a senior. It's all too much. This intruding Genie is promising that he's going to help me, but that's ridiculous. Everything is horrible.

My text message dings. Oh no, it's my ogre boss, Jana. What could she want at 10:00 p.m.? "Can you be at work at 7 tomorrow morning? I've got depositions and a brief due, so I'm going to need extra help."

Hello? Is she serious? Now that I'm not getting married, it's time to seriously look for another job. I don't even know where to start. My whole life is so janked up. I hate it all. But since I need to pay rent until I find other work, I agree to her selfish request.

"Okay, I'll see you at 7," I text back.

My friend Ellie texts me again so we can make final plans about our outing to the Vesta Home Show on Saturday. Beautiful houses and interior designs are some of the few things I do enjoy. Ellie and I have attended this show together for the last three years, and it is one of my favorite yearly events. Thinking of the beautiful rooms I'll see on Saturday is something I always look forward to. But then the thought appears that I am not getting the beautiful house that I thought Leland's salary was going to buy me, and I can instantly feel my spirit sink. I'm going to be a spinster and never have children. And tomorrow I have to return to my dreadful job.

I just noticed something. When I thought about going to the Vesta Home Show, I felt temporarily better. And then when I realized I am *not* getting my own new beautiful house (in addition to being an old maid), I felt lousy again. I realize that this is an example of what the Genie told me, that my *thoughts produce my emotions*. What else did he say? He said I can learn to listen in to the Parade of Thoughts that March across My Brain, my self-talk, and if my thoughts are negative or upsetting, I can Play Hot Potatoes and Move into Another Room in My Brain by thinking another thought. But is that realistic?

During my conversation with Ellie, I was not upset when I thought about the Vesta Home Show. But the moment that conversation in my brain was over, my self-talk reverted to my ruminations about how crummy my life is, and the dark cloud returned.

Admittedly, I would like to find a path away from this continual black cloud that hovers over me. According to the Genie, I *produce* that black cloud by my continual ruminating of negative thoughts. He says that thoughts create chemical reactions, and by thinking negative thoughts for a long time, I have created a chemical imbalance in my brain.

Then he made the audacious statement that my brain can heal when I stop thinking negative thoughts all the time and learn a more *optimistic thinking style*. But honestly, how does one *not think* negative thoughts when all their circumstances are disastrous? Escaping my chronic disappointment and discouragement seems impossible.

I pour a glass of wine and settle down to do some online shopping and read my design magazines—the only comforts I know.

My younger sister, Bailey, texts me: "I hope you will bring balloons and flowers Friday night, as well as a hot appetizer. With these two little girls, I don't have much time to get out and shop. Are you going to bake Mom a special cake?"

Maybe I should ask her if I can come over, clean her house, and set her table, too. She seems incapable of doing anything. I've tried to tell Bailey that we just need to go to a restaurant and divide the bill, but she always squawks at that suggestion and says that she and Daniel don't have money in their entertainment budget for those kinds of events. They certainly found money for a trip to Hawaii.

I do enjoy baking, however, and I have made some exotic cakes for Bailey's daughters as well as other family members and friends. I made a Barbie doll mansion cake, a *Toy Story* cake with Jessie and Woody, a cake with a *Frozen* theme, and a *Little Mermaid* cake. I probably should not have started that tradition since Bailey assumes I will do it every year from now to eternity.

A text message dings from my mom. Oh, joy.

"I wanted you to know I met a new gentleman friend, Henry, and Bailey said I can invite him to my birthday party Friday night. I hope you will dress up and do your hair and makeup. Your hair is usually a mess."

That familiar icky feeling creeps over me whenever my mother criticizes me. There's no way to shield myself from her darts. On top of that, my mother is entirely out of line to invite a potential new boyfriend to a family dinner.

How can I separate myself from my mother? How? What should I do to change my life? Something has to be done. I can't go on being this miserable.

Just before I switch off the light, I check my phone again to see if Leland has texted me. The bum. He used me. He flat-out used me. I hate him. I hate a lot of things. Leland and his pathetic mother. Bethany texting Leland. My mother's critical spirit. Paying Shelby's half of the rent. My job. Being single and childless. My wrinkles.

I'm miserable, just miserable.

(The summaries of the Genie's teaching can be found in the back of this book.)

Lesson 2

Quarantining What's Missing and Disappointing (the WMDs) and Reframing, Refuting, and Replacing the WMDs

Friday evening, August 24

Even though I showed up at work yesterday at 7:00 a.m., Jana didn't even thank me. After I got off work, I took some online tests to try to figure out what type of job I'm best suited for. It seems my main interests are interior design and cooking (no surprise there). How stupid I was to count on marrying Leland and not grow in my career. I am such a dunce. How I regret the last ten years!

After earning a degree in interior design, I mistakenly went to work for a medium-priced furniture store. I ended up *selling* furniture—a sofa here, a bed there—but had no opportunity to design. And the furniture was cheap, which royally annoyed me. But because I was going through a bad breakup (the story of my life), I left that job and took an easier, more soothing job arranging flowers in a flower shop. Not only was the work stress-free, but the beauty of the flowers was actually healing to me. The florist job was intended to be a transition until I could return to the design world. I had no idea I would become the manager and stay for three years.

Then at age twenty-eight, a flower shop customer offered me a job as the office administrator of her divorce law firm. Since she was offering almost twice what I was making—although I was only working thirty hours a week—I took the job. In the first year, Jana was difficult to work for but tolerable. But as her case load increased, so did her stress level. Slowly but gradually, she kept adding to my duties without increasing my pay. A year ago, after three years without a raise, I discussed it with her. She explained that she couldn't afford to give me a raise at the moment but would consider it next year. At that point, I seriously thought about quitting and trying to go back to graduate school for design, but by then I was dating Leland and feeling pretty confident about a proposal, so I decided to wait and do nothing.

That was the path to my current pathetic situation. If I try to get back in design, all I can hope for is an entry-level job. I can detect that familiar dark cloud of discouragement starting to descend—that I will never find a job I like and get adequately paid.

I mean, I had a *life plan*—a good one. I would get married early, have four perfect children (at least one or two would be girls), and play tennis twice a week. My house would be cutting-edge design, and my time would be spent mothering, shopping, reading, volunteering, and having interesting people over for dinner parties while my husband climbed his career ladder. Yes, that was my original, wonderful life plan.

But it's been disappointment after disappointment. Never in a million years did I think I would get dumped at thirty-two, have no career, be deep in debt, and still be entangled with my neurotic mother and thoughtless sister. Everything is terribly disheartening. The familiar emotional landslide begins to creep over me.

Oh my! There it is! The Parade! I hear the Parade Marching across My Brain—the incessant, negative Parade. Let's see if any of the Genie's suggestions work. I'll try to use Playing Hot Potatoes as well as Moving into Another Room in My Brain by thinking about something else.

Getting on *YouTube*, I watch a ten-minute video on the newest ideas for designing a kitchen. What novel and creative ideas the video has!

Actually, Playing Hot Potatoes and Moving into Another Room in My Brain worked, and I was soon absorbed in the video and forgot all about my pathetic job and life. Of course, when the video ended, my ruminating returned. Maybe the Genie's little tricks work for a bit, but they won't work permanently for the major disasters going on in my life.

The plan tonight is to escape my mother's birthday party as soon as I can and then spend more time shining up my resume and looking online for a new job. Leaving to drive to Bailey's house for the birthday party, I check to make sure I have everything. Flowers, balloons, a present, a cake (nothing special), a sausage-and-cheese appetizer, and my scrumptious spinach casserole. I've got everything. I wonder what time I can leave.

I still can't believe Mom just got a new boyfriend and has already invited him to a family dinner. The only thing I know about him is that he's a widower, seventy-nine, and loaded. Seventy-nine is a little old since my mother is only sixty-one, but a big bank account erases the years in my mother's eyes.

As I walk in, my mother is all hugs and kisses like we're the closest mother-daughter team in the world. Behind her is a short, little, bald man, round like Santa Claus. He's wearing wire-rimmed glasses and looks like the grandpa commonly portrayed in children's books.

"Hi, Darby," he says. "I'm Henry. You are pretty like your mother." It's true that my mother does have good bone structure, but with all of her Botox and collagen injections, she looks almost frozen to me.

"Hi, Henry," I say, thinking that it would be fun to add, "Are you as rich as my mother hopes you are?"

"Darby, can you help me in the kitchen?" my mother asks in her sweet sing-song voice. When I get in there, she scolds me. "I thought I told you to dress up. Those jeans have holes in them." My mother thinks the clothes you wear are more important than your character. Although she's sixty-one, she still wears skirts that are too short and spaghetti strap tops, embracing styles that women her age should have given up twenty-five years ago.

I respond to my mother's concerns about my jeans. "These are very expensive designer jeans, Mom. They are called 'distressed.' I paid $250 for these."

"You did not!" she said, as though her statement was notarized. "Those look like you got them at the thrift store."

Bailey overhears and for once comes to my rescue. "Mom, she's right. The distressed look is very popular."

My mother shakes her head and goes back into the living room with her sing-song voice to carry on with Henry.

Bailey calls everyone to the table, and my mother starts pointing to seats, telling everyone where to sit. Even though there are five adults, my mother does 80 percent of the talking. I guess she's nervous with Daddy Moneybags here.

The conversation is pleasant, going from the World Series to Bailey's daughter's dance recital to Henry's multi-million-dollar plumbing business that his two sons are now running.

"My oldest son, Hank, basically runs the business since I'm officially retired," he says. "I still show up every morning, read the *Wall Street Journal* in my office, drink coffee, and annoy everyone with my questions."

Henry is kind of cute and funny in a grandfatherly sort of way. My mother carries on about how smart he must be to run such a large business. Henry doesn't hate it, for sure.

At one lull in the conversation, Henry turns to me and says, "Darby, as cute as you are, you must have a boyfriend."

All eyes fall on me. My first thought is to say, "No, I'm considering becoming a nun."

But lucky me, my mom comes to the rescue and answers for me. "Darby was just dating a doctor," and after a long pause, adds in a sad tone, "but I guess it didn't work out." It was as if she just told the table I have an incurable disease.

"Why, I wish I'd known," declares Henry. "I have a single son, Hank."

Without missing a beat, Mom suggests, "Maybe he could come over now and meet Darby."

Before I can even get my mind wrapped around what's happening, Henry is texting his son and inviting him over.

"He's free," Henry announces. "He's on his way."

"Uh, uh, well, uh, that's nice," I say, "but I have to leave early tonight. Can you please text him back and tell him I'd love to meet him some other time?"

"Oh, Darby, you can stay a little longer," my mother says like she's giving me permission. Apparently, she thinks that maybe she and I have both won the lottery. "Wouldn't that just be adorable, Henry, if our children hooked up?"

My brother-in-law, Daniel, can't help but laugh out loud. My mom has no idea what the modern day version of "hooked up" means.

Realizing that I'm losing control like a car with no brakes heading downhill, I try to intercede again. "Henry, it's almost time for me to leave. Please text him and tell him we'll do it another time."

Henry glances at his phone and says, "He just texted that he's five minutes away. Can't you stay five minutes, Darby?"

Now I'm stuck. My first thought is to wonder how old Hank is since his father is seventy-nine. But there's no way I can ask that question. Glancing at my mother, I see her squinting her eyes at me as if to say, "Don't screw this up, Darby. I'm warning you."

Eight minutes later, the doorbell rings. Mom says, "Darby, why don't you answer the door and invite Hank in?"

Immediately sensing how awkward that would be, Bailey jumps up and offers to go to the door. Bailey opens the door and graciously welcomes Hank inside. I can't see Hank yet, but I look outside the dining room window and notice a shiny, new, two-seater Mercedes Benz. I can hear Hank's voice. He does have a nice voice—in fact, a beautiful voice like a TV news anchor. But a lot of ugly men have gorgeous voices, right?

Bailey and Hank round the corner. Why, he looks about fifty years old! Now admittedly, he's a good-looking fifty-year-old with a fabulous tan and gorgeous, expensive clothes. But he's probably fifty!

His eyes dance as he looks at me like he is the cat and I am the canary.

Bailey gets Hank a plate of food, and the group continues with small talk. Henry is mainly running the conversation now, with my mother complimenting everything he says.

Henry talks about what a fine father Hank is, and how Hank's son, Kyle, graduated with a 4.0 from high school. Then Henry mentions Katie, Hank's little five-year-old daughter.

"There's a big break between those two kids," I say, wondering about the wife. There's some silence and Hank says, "Yes, Kyle is from my first wife, and Katie is from my second."

No one says anything, but I'm thinking, *Are these divorces? Were you widowed?*

But Henry helps me out. "Good thing Hank is a multi-millionaire since he has to pay two alimonies."

Hank likes the comment. He's not embarrassed in the least that he has had two divorces. I know people make mistakes and get divorced, but twice? Again, probably-fifty-year-old Hank eyes me like I'm a summer lemonade he can't wait to sip. It grosses me out.

Mom and I go in the kitchen. As she cuts the dessert, I tell her I'm tired and I'm leaving. Her eyes flash with disapproval. "Darby! Hank just got here!"

"Mom, he's fifty-ish, divorced twice, and has a five-year-old. I wouldn't get into that alligator swamp if you paid me a billion dollars. I told you I'm leaving."

"I forbid it," she says. "You march in there and act nice."

Looking at my mother with as much composure as I can muster, I reply, "I'll tell everyone goodnight, and then I'm leaving." I walk back into the dining room, tell everyone it's been a busy week, and that I'm headed home. I barely make eye contact with Hank, but I can see he is disappointed.

Following me to my car, my mother says, "We will discuss this again, Darby McChesney. I'm appalled."

"Good night, Mom," I say, quietly. "I'm almost thirty-three, not thirteen, and it's time you realize you aren't in charge of me anymore. You don't get to order me around." I get in my car and leave. I'm shaking again, much like the time my mother stormed into my apartment and demanded that I not pursue a father-daughter relationship with my dad.

How would the Genie ever be able to help me deal with a tsunami like my mother? There is no possible way. Still shaking, I continue driving toward my apartment. Remembering that Shelby moved out yesterday, I'm glad to have the apartment to myself.

While driving, I think about Leland's rejection, that there are no good men around to marry when you're my age, that I've wasted so much time with losers, that I'm trapped and bored in my job, and that my mother is delirious. I have the worst life!

Unlocking my apartment door, I am startled to see the Genie sitting in the lotus position on a large cushion. "Whew!" the Genie says. "That was intense with your mother. I will address the topic of relationships in Lesson 9. Are you ready to begin tonight's lesson?"

Lesson 9 seems like a long time off, but obviously, I'm not setting the agenda.

"Let's first review what you learned in your first lesson," he says. "You learned that thoughts produce emotions. Therefore, you are the *producer, not the victim*, of your emotions. If you are emotionally low, it's because you have allowed your brain to *think about* what you don't have, what is not working, what's missing, what's disappointing, and what's not right. Thinking negative thoughts guarantees negative emotions."

He pauses briefly to see if I'm tracking and then continues.

"Also in Lesson 1, you learned to listen in on your self-talk (the Parade that Marches across Your Brain) and to interrupt it (Play Hot Potatoes) by intentionally thinking about something else (Moving into Another Room in Your Brain). When you notice the negative thought, brush it away as you would a spark on your sweatshirt from a campfire. Train yourself to notice and immediately reject—versus accept—negative messages."

"I guess I *sort of* learned all that," I say. I'm still not exactly sure how to keep my disappointment from invading and overtaking my mind.

"Good. Let's begin Lesson 2. Please open your Quartz Journal."[13]

I don't have any better strategy to deal with my sorry life, so why not?

"All humans develop a *life plan*, Young Darby—a plan of how they want their life to unfold. But then, of course, as you know, things do not usually go according to the life plan," he says.

I'll say.

"There is often a fantasy," he says, "that life should proceed without suffering. But the truth is that there are often many circumstances or situations in one's life that are missing and disappointing. In *Happy School*, we call What's Missing and Disappointing in one's life the WMDs. And since thoughts produce emotions, one will be emotionally down if one repeatedly ruminates about their WMDs."

I realize that I think about What's Missing and Disappointing all day long. I hardly think about anything else.

"Today's lesson has three aspects," the Genie continues. "The first aspect is that you must think about your WMDs *by appointment only*. That is, you only think about your WMDs when you're in one of the following three situations."

I hope the three situations are morning, noon, and night.

"The first situation," he says, "is when you are researching solutions and writing about them in your Quartz Journal. The second situation is when you are talking to someone who might have answers or solutions. And the third situation is when you are in prayer."[14]

"Only those three situations?" I ask, thinking how impossible it would be for me to confine thinking about my problems to only those three occasions.

---

13. This exercise, Rethinking Your WMDs, is found at the back of this book in the list for your Quartz Journal.
14. In prayer, we are to roll our burdens on the Lord. Humans are not built to carry heavy burdens in life. The command is, "Let not your heart be troubled" (John 14:1 NKJV).

"Yes, only those three times," he says. "When a WMD descends into your thoughts, do as you learned in Lesson 1, Play Hot Potatoes and immediately Move into Another Room in Your Brain by thinking about something else."

I've got a truckload of WMDs. I'm single. I'm childless. My mother is deranged. I hate my job. My skin and eggs are aging at the speed of light. I'm in colossal debt. And that's just the tip of my WMD iceberg.

"Quarantining your WMDs is truly magical," he says. "It keeps you from letting your WMDs dominate the landscape of your mind."

Magical? He exaggerates so much.

"When you quarantine a thought," he says, "think of putting it in a box with a lid on it and then putting the box on a shelf until your next problem-solving session.[15] Your problems are like neighborhood bullies, but they can be corralled and put in detention. They are not in charge."

Uh, so far they have been.

"When you're ready to proactively problem-solve, take the lid off the particular problem box and work on it. When you are through, put the lid back on the problem box, and put it back on the shelf."

I wonder, what would I think about instead? I stew in my negative thoughts all day long.

"Genie, what if negative thoughts keep coming back?" I ask.

"Bar the doors of your mind against negative thoughts as you would bar your house against a thief. You must quit thinking about what you *lack*. Command your mind to quarantine your WMDs and only think about them during one of those three specific times."

I guess I could try.

"Constant ruminating on negative and discouraging thoughts will leave a chemical imbalance in your brain. When you quarantine your WMDs, the chemical imbalance of your brain can begin to heal."[16]

---

15. Another good analogy to think of when quarantining your WMDs is to think of locking them in a vault until your next problem-solving session.

16. If you are currently on antidepressants, do not withdraw or get off them without a plan from your mental health provider.

I'm sure it's all a little more difficult than that.

"The second aspect of tonight's lesson is to reframe, refute, or replace your WMDs in your Quartz Journal."

What craziness is he talking about now?

"In your Quartz Journal, make three columns on the page titled Rethinking Your WMDs. On the left, list your main WMDs."

I've got plenty to choose from.

"In the center column, write Steps of Action. That's where you will brainstorm steps you can take to problem-solve."

I write that down.

"Then label the column on the far right Reframe, Refute, and Replace. This is where you will write down possible new interpretations about your WMDs."

Again, I write as he directs.

"Insist that your self-talk fights to find the good things about your situation," he says. "For example, under your concern that you're still single, you could write down that you're glad you're not married to the wrong person."

I don't know if I can swallow his positive Mary Poppins approach.

"Humans tell themselves, 'This obstacle is too big. This trial is insurmountable.' In contrast, you must tell yourself that opportunity often shows up in the darkest places and, instead, expect favor to break through.[17] Refuse to believe there is no hope.[18] Opportunities are often hidden in seemingly unfortunate circumstances and impossibilities."[19]

I'm the Queen of unfortunate circumstances.

"*Disappointing* circumstances are inevitable," he says, "but *discouragement is optional* because you can choose your thoughts."[20]

---

17. The God who can gather the sea in jars, get Mary pregnant without a man, and walk on water can (and still does) perform miracles. Children don't ask for bread and receive scorpions. They get toast with honey.

18. "For we walk by faith, not by sight" (2 Corinthians 5:7 NKJV).

19. While in a Roman prison, Paul penned, "Whatever is true…think about such things" (Philippians 4:8 NIV).

20. Scripture is filled with verses instructing us to not let negative thoughts and emotions rule. Examples: "Do not fear, for I am with you*"* (Isaiah 41:10 NIV). "Let not your heart be troubled" (John 14:1 NKJV). "Be anxious for nothing (Philippians 4:6 NKJV).

There he goes again, saying outlandish things such as *discouragement is optional.*

"Humans must learn to stop blaming circumstances for their unhappy heart," he says. "A victim mentality is poisonous. You have the power to choose which thoughts you think, and thus you possess the power to *choose* the emotional environment in your mind."

What I keep hearing him say is that I'm responsible for my unhappiness because of my current thinking patterns. But he's wrong.

"The assignment for now is to figure out what your major WMDs are and write them in the left column on your Rethinking Your WMDs page in your Quartz Journal. Brainstorm possible solutions (Steps of Action) in the center column. And then, in the right column, write down sentences where you dial down your negative thinking by reframing, refuting, and replacing your negative self-talk."

"Okay," I say as I quickly scribble down the first four WMDs that come to mind. "But can you help me reframe, refute, and replace a few of my WMDs?"

Here is what I wrote down:

1. I'm an old maid, and it looks like I always will be.
2. My mother is actually crazy, and she torments me.
3. I hate my job. I hate hate hate my job.
4. I'm in debt, and I'm eating up my dad's inheritance.

"For example," I begin, "what would I write next to 'I'm an old maid, and it looks like I always will be'?"

"To dispute or refute that WMD," he says, "you could write, 'Many women get married in their thirties and have large families.' Or write down, 'There are many desirable and eligible men that would enjoy a woman like me.'"

I wish he would find them and give them my phone number.

"What would I write down next to 'My mother is actually crazy, and she torments me'?"

The Genie responds, "Write down, 'Many people have emotionally or mentally unbalanced parents and learn how to deal effectively with them.'"

Where is that manual, I wonder?

"And what about my terrible job? What do I say about that?"

"We are going to address that issue in Lesson 5, but for now, write, 'People move from bad jobs to delightful jobs all the time, and I can learn the skills to do so.'"

He acts like it's all so easy-breezy.

"Here's the last WMD I wrote down," I say. "'I'm in debt, and I'm eating up my dad's inheritance.'"

The Genie again has no shortage of answers. "Write down, 'People are in serious debt all the time and learn how to reverse the problem.'"

Actually, I have thought about buying a couple Dave Ramsey books.

"What I want you to see, Young Darby, is that there is abundant hope and there are answers to your dilemmas.[21] You have not explored answers proactively but instead have let negative thinking keep you in a locked cage. We are going to break open that cage and see that there are many answers to your multiple problems."

It's easy to throw around words like *hope* and *answers*, but it's a lot harder to prove it.

"Life will try to crush you, but you can live life uncrushed if you learn to control your thoughts.[22] Every time you think of a WMD, record it, problem-solve, and then reframe, refute, and replace it."[23]

That sounds like a lot of work.

"The third aspect of tonight's lesson," he continues, "is that some humans have a tendency to 'awfulize' and 'catastrophize' the things in their life that are missing and disappointing."

---

21. Refute the beliefs that are driving the fear, insecurity, or discouragement. Remember how big God is, how He is able, and that He cares. Remember that He answers prayer. Remember that He is "able to do exceedingly abundantly above all that we ask or think" (Ephesians 3:20 NKJV).

22. "Thou wilt keep him in perfect peace whose mind is stayed on thee" (Isaiah 26:3 KJV).

23. "With God all things are possible" (Matthew 19:26 KJV).

"But it's true that it *is* awful that I'm old and single and that there are no good men around," I say.

"Young Darby, you can *dial down* your self-talk that says your situation is awful and terrible. You can learn to say to yourself, 'I would *prefer* to have such and such,' but you must not *catastrophize* circumstances. A plane crash is a catastrophe, but the Internet being down is not. Getting ink on your new cream sofa is not, and neither is your sister not doing her part for Thanksgiving. Even getting fired or getting left in a relationship is not catastrophic. Hurtful? Terribly. But not catastrophic. People recover and heal all the time from painful break-ups, betrayals, and disappointing relationships. It's okay to have strong feelings of sadness, irritation, and concern. Desiring, wishing, and preferring are also appropriate responses."

That seems rather cold-blooded. Maybe genies don't understand the intensity of human relationships. I think getting left in a relationship when your eggs are getting ancient is a catastrophe whether he agrees or not.

"Dialing down your self-talk is a skill to learn," he says. "Again, tell yourself that situations are *unwanted* and *not preferred* but not cataclysmic."

I remember last week when my mother called me and said, "Something horrible has happened!" Immediately, I thought maybe something horrendous had happened to one of Bailey's little girls. Then my mother continued, "Someone stole one of my dinner rings!" I remember thinking that having one of your rings stolen is certainly annoying and unwanted, but it is *neither horrible nor a crisis*. I can always see principles better in other people's lives than I can see them in my own.

"View your WMDs as something you want very badly," the Genie went on, "but don't *awfulize* the situation and tell yourself *you must have* it or life is horrible. People can learn to live joyfully with a host of problems by learning how to think correctly about their problems."

Live joyfully? That's a joke.

"Of course, no one likes failure, rejection, betrayal, or discomfort, but you can stand them. You won't collapse. You can still be reasonably happy with unfortunate circumstances."

He's wrong. I might collapse.

"Tell yourself that you would *prefer* to not have a neurotic mother. You would *prefer* to be married, and you would *prefer* to have a job you like. But the human condition has trials and tribulations,[24] and you must accept a portion. To insist that life be pain-free is to be demanding and entitled."

He is not the most compassionate genie, that's for sure. But I do see that I call my circumstances devastating. I wonder if I could dial back the way I talk to myself.

"You have to listen in on your self-talk, Young Darby, and catch yourself saying how horrible and terrible your circumstances are. Remember, saying that your circumstances are 'not preferred' and 'not wanted' is the correct way to talk to yourself."

"Genie, those ideas might work on some people, but I'm afraid I'm too broken to be fixed. I was labeled clinically depressed at one time." There. That will show him that I'm not the ordinary, discouraged person. I'm a chronically, eternally disappointed, and damaged person.

"That is simply not correct," he says. "Your mind is plastic, as I said earlier, which means it can change. You can completely rewire your brain. Remember the example of the schoolyard paths? By choosing which thoughts to quarantine and which new thoughts to insert (what I'm going to teach you in the upcoming lessons), you can actually renew your mind and become a different person. Humans master their minds and change their thinking patterns all the time."

A different person? Right. Yeah, the chance of changing from this discouraged person into a happy person would be another case of turning water into wine.[25]

---

24. "In this world you will have trouble. But take heart! I have overcome the world" (John 16:33 NIV).
25. God is still in the business of turning water into wine. "Beauty for ashes" is His specialty (Isaiah 61:3 NKJV).

"Can't I just take some of the new anti-depressants?" I ask.[26]

"I am very distressed when I hear that," he says. "You *must* do the work to learn to *think* differently. Thinking differently is the answer to overcoming discouragement. There's someone walking up to your front door, and it's time for me to get a massage in Thailand. I will be back soon with Lesson 3." And with that, he dissolved into a funnel of air and disappeared.

Walking to the front door, I'm startled to see Leland. He must be here to tell me he's made the biggest mistake of his life. Oh! My! Goodness! Leland is here to beg me to get back together.

Still standing in the doorway, he mumbles "hey" in a low voice.

"I'm surprised to see you," I say. He doesn't say anything, and I ask him if he wants to come in.

"Thanks," he says as he walks in.

"Want something to eat?" I ask. Leland is always hungry.

"I just got back from dinner, so I'm not hungry," he says.

Just casually making conversation, similar to how one would ask someone how their day was, I say, "Where did you eat?"

Leland's restaurants are always take-out Mexican or American, never anything expensive.

"Actually, I ate at the Capital Grille," he says.

That got my attention. In the two years we dated, Leland never took me anywhere swanky like the Capital Grille. "Really?" I say. "That's a fabulous restaurant. What was the occasion?" Maybe his office went out and treated everyone.

He shuffles around, looks down, and slowly searches for his words. "Well, I, uh, I took one of our friends out to dinner."

Now I'm really confused. One of our friends? I can't even begin to imagine this. Who would he take?

---

26. If you are currently on antidepressants, do not suddenly stop. Talk to your medical advisor, and develop a plan to gradually withdraw. In many studies, exercise is as effective as antidepressants in reducing depression. See Lesson 8 on Worry and Fear to learn more about how healthy habits impact your emotional health.

"One of our friends?" I ask. I'm still trying not to be nosey but just to make regular conversation. Maybe one of his friends, Kyle or Elijah, had a birthday.

"Uh, yeah, well, uh, Bethany," he says, still looking down and shuffling again.

"Bethany?" I ask in utter disbelief.

"Yeah, she was free for dinner, so we went," he says.

"You took Bethany to dinner at Capital Grille?" I ask, still in shock.

"Well, yeah," he says. "I told her you and I broke up, and she said she would love to get together and talk if I needed to. So I suggested we go to dinner tonight."

"So you talked to her about us?" I ask, barely able to stand up.

"Actually, we didn't mention you," he says.

The situation is now becoming crystal clear. Leland and I break up on Wednesday night, Bethany throws herself at Leland on Thursday, and then tonight he takes her to a top restaurant in town. The insult of it all feels like a cold tub of ice water being poured on my head. And they didn't even mention me. He has already moved on!

Speechless, I merely look at Leland. Finally, he looks up at me and speaks. "Well, uh, the reason I'm here, is, uh, is because, uh, my mom was wondering if you would give me back that emerald ring I gave you for Christmas. It belonged to my grandmother, so it has sentimental value."

His mom was wondering? He's such a coward that he can't even ask for it without throwing his mom into the scenario.

"I've still got it," I say, reeling from how disrespected I feel. I don't feel hurt that Leland doesn't love me. I feel offended. To me, Bethany is a mousy bore. And she is *supposedly* my friend. But moving in on him a day after we break up? Pitiful.

"So can I have it back?" he asks.

Infuriated over the whole situation—Leland, his mean mom, his complete selfishness in using me for two years, and now his instant attraction to boring Bethany—I decide again to take the high road, give back the ring, and wash my hands of anything to do with Leland.

Without saying anything, I walk into my bedroom, get the ring out of my jewelry box, walk back to Leland, and hand it to him. He holds it in his hand and stares at it. "Thanks," he says. "My mom will appreciate this."

I'm ashamed of what I'm thinking about his mother right now. My heart is pretty wicked sometimes.

"Goodnight, Leland," I say, letting him know the visit is over. He gets it and walks toward the front door. I open the door, and he walks out. "Thanks again," he says as he walks out.

I don't say anything as I close the door. But my heart is pounding, and I'm furious. My emotional fury is probably an eight out of ten. Walking into my bedroom, I decide to see if any of the Genie's teaching can help me. I pull out my Quartz Journal and find the Rethinking My WMDs page with the three columns. With a shaky hand, I write this in the left WMD column:

I feel disrespected and used. I feel angry that I have been mistreated by Leland and his judgmental mom. I feel betrayed by my supposed friend, Bethany.

Now I move to the center column, Steps of Action. I can't even breathe much less think of any Steps of Action. So I proceed to the far right, the Reframe, Refute, and Replace column. Staring at the paper, I try to think of something. Slowly, I write:

Leland was a good catch on paper, but he was not a soul mate. In fact, he bored me, and his best attributes were his salary and good looks. It is best that we broke up because now I am free to find a person I truly love.

Continuing to stare at the paper, I add:

I never liked or trusted Bethany, so I should not be surprised she is moving in on Leland. I am not losing a friend, because she never was a friend.

I start to close my Quartz Journal but instead add one more thought:

Breaking up with Leland and his going out with Bethany are not a catastrophe, so I must not "awfulize" the situation. The situation is unwanted and not preferred, but it is not a catastrophe.

I still hate Leland and his mom, and I don't know what to do about that,[27] but I do notice that my fiery emotions are calming down. The thought that maybe now I can find someone better suited for me than Leland—someone I love and who loves me—is a positive thought, even though at the moment it feels impossible.[28]

Now that I've reframed the situation the best I can, what am I supposed to do? I'm supposed to put my problem—my hatred for Leland, Bethany, and his mom—into a box with a lid on a shelf until I can deal with it rationally. That is, I'm to quarantine it. Okay, I can do that. Then what? Oh! Move into Another Room in My Brain. Let's see. What can I think about?

With the Vesta Home Show tomorrow, I think I'll get on some of my favorite designer websites like Suzanne Kasler's or Elizabeth Gullett's to get my thoughts on a neutral subject. Yes, I'll do that. Grabbing my laptop and plopping down on my bed, I pour myself a glass of wine. (My drinking is another snake in the grass I've got to address at some point.)[29] The wine dials down my emotions, but Moving into Another Room in My Brain definitely helps, too.

Right before I turn off the light, I notice there's a text from my mother: "You were so rude to Hank. And I can tell that Henry is now pulling away since you were rude. I know you're upset because you're getting old and you're single, but you have no right to treat me like this."

Taking out my Quartz Journal again and turning to the Rethinking My WMDs page, I add this:

---

27. The Genie will address resentment in Lesson 8.
28. "With God all things are possible" (Matthew 19:26 NKJV).
29. Lesson 4 is about self-discipline and overcoming bad habits.

My mother drives me crazy because, well, she is crazy. I'm angry at her all the time. I wish I didn't have to be involved with her except on Thanksgiving and Christmas. I wish I had a sweet, patient, supportive mother. I'm messed up because I had such a bad role model for a mother.

Then under the Steps of Action column, I write:

Maybe I should see a counselor to help me think through this and set some healthy boundaries.

Then I remember that the Genie said he is going to help me with my relationships in Lesson 9. I will wait and see if his advice helps and then decide if I still need to see a counselor.

Continuing in my Quartz Journal, I move to the right column, and under Reframe, Refute, and Replace, I write:

I'm an adult now, and my mother does not get 24/7 access to me. I decide the boundaries.

And then I also write:

The Genie is teaching me how to be emotionally healthy. I still have much to learn in Happy School, *so maybe I will get more help dealing with my mother.*

Writing helps a little. Wine helps a lot.
Goodnight, world. Goodnight, sad, sad world.

Lesson 3

Don't Assign Negative Interpretations to External Circumstances

Saturday morning, August 25

At least on Saturday mornings I don't have to report to Sergeant Jana. Although I don't feel especially well this morning (those two glasses of wine), I've agreed to meet my friend Whitney for a walk. After that, there is actually something I'm looking forward to—going to the Vesta Home Show with Ellie.

Throwing on my walking garb, I glance in the mirror before heading out the door. I remind myself of the witch in *Sleeping Beauty*—haggard and mean. There I go again, saying negative things *to* myself *about* myself. I don't have time to write that down in my Quartz Journal, but let's see if I can problem-solve or refute that in my head. How about, *I must start taking better care of my skin. I could get professional facials, buy an organic skin care line, and do masks at home. Also, I can research skin nutrition.*

Huh. Not bad. That was actually helpful. My little refutation. *Good job*, I say to myself. I smile and look in the mirror. I still look terrible and think I should probably put on some makeup, but seeing the time on my phone, I realize I'm already late. So out the door I go, bare face and all.

It's true that most of my thoughts are filled with WMDs such as how Leland mistreated me, how I hate my job, how I hate being single, and that there are no good men left for me. The Genie said he'll teach me some good thoughts to think. What could they possibly be? This all sounds very difficult, and I don't like difficult things.

Pulling into the Shelby Farms Greenline parking area, I see Whitney, and we start our walk. The moment our feet hit the trail, she begins gushing about her life like a thoroughbred madly racing out of the gate when the shot is fired at the Kentucky Derby. Whitney, who is actually a faithful friend, often talks too much about herself, and today is no exception. She begins with stories about her dog (dogs are fine, but getting their teeth professionally cleaned is ridiculous). Then she moves to her new skin care regimen (which I'd be more interested in if it were organic since I hate parabens). Finally, she dissects the drama at her place of employment and gives me the latest updates on her toddlers' antics. After forty-five minutes of nodding and inserting an occasional polite question, I'm glad our walk is over. I hear myself complaining to myself that even my best friends are not what I'd hoped, and I feel frustrated I didn't get a chance to talk about my hot mess of a life.

As we walk to our cars, Whitney asks, "Do you have time to go to Stax for breakfast? Pete (her husband) said he would take care of the kiddos for two hours, so I still have an hour left."

Since I'm itching to tell her my saga with Leland, I am tempted to go, even though I look horrible. "Do you have any makeup with you?" I ask. She doesn't, but she convincingly adds, "Who could we see? Our parents' friends? Come on. Let's go."

Really wanting to vent about Leland's mistreatment, I consent. The air inside Stax smells like pancakes and freshly brewed coffee. My mood improves as I realize how much I enjoy going to breakfast on Saturday mornings. The thought that my Saturday mornings for the last two years have been spent helping Leland do his laundry and his chores makes me feel sad (and angry), and again, I fume because I didn't have two years to waste.

As we're waiting for a table, I see something that ignites my heart rate like a match lighting charcoal drenched with lighter fluid. It's Leland and Bethany having a cozy little breakfast. She is in stage-worthy entertainment mode, making some sort of wild gestures with her hands. He is leaning back in his chair, smiling approvingly at her, obviously enjoying the show. Her workout top has a cut-out back, and her sports bra is showing. It looks like her yoga pants have been spray-painted on, and you can see every indentation and bump. Her hair is casually wadded up in a top knot bun, but she has on full Melania Trump makeup. Again, I notice how Leland is royally enjoying her antics.

Turning quickly around, I whisper to Whitney, "Whitney, we need to leave."

"Why?" she asks loudly.

With Whitney's volume, something in Bethany alerts her to turn around. Seeing me, Bethany gives a little wave and turns back to Leland. Then he glances up and sees me. He looks like a bank teller who just discovered his next customer is an armed robber. My heart is beating faster than any aerobic activity safely allows.

At that second, the hostess walks up to Whitney and me and says, "Follow me, please. Your table is ready." I think about darting for the door, but Bethany would love to tell our Sorority Supper Club that story. So I follow the hostess, feeling like a prisoner led to a firing squad. And where, of course, does she take us but to a table that is actually within earshot of the new lovebirds.

Whitney's light bulb finally goes on. "What is that?" she asks in a very low, surprised tone. Whitney had no idea that we had broken up, so seeing Leland with someone else was quite the news.

I want to stop by their table and say to Bethany, "How nice you're going out to eat. But in two weeks, he'll have you doing his laundry."

Bethany and Leland are uncomfortable with me there—gorgeous me with no makeup on—and they stand up to leave.

Again, the thought goes through my mind, and I want to say, "If he gives you his grandmother's ring, just know it's a loan." But again, I rarely say the sarcastic, mean things I think.

Whitney is all ears as I lay out the events of the last three days. During the whole story, she merely shakes her head in disbelief. After I am finished explaining the situation, her summary statement is spot on: "Darby, I know you don't like your fertility clock ticking, but you're definitely relieved to be rid of him." Whitney does talk a lot about herself, but she makes up for it when you need a friend to truly listen and empathize.

After saying goodbye to Whitney, I drive home. I think about what Whitney said, that I'm relieved to be rid of Leland. Is that true? I've been so focused on being single and being humiliated by the breakup and his immediate attraction to Bethany that I haven't truly processed how I feel about our separation. Am I humiliated or relieved? I guess I don't know what I am. All I know is that I'm in a wad.

I've got about thirty minutes before I need to start getting ready to meet Ellie at the Vesta Home Show. **Entering the apartment, I lay my keys on the counter and am startled to see the Genie in my den, sitting on the floor, drinking some Babylonian tea.** Honestly, I have had enough drama for one morning and would rather skip another one of his intense lessons. Apparently, the Genie decides when school is in session.

"I've been waiting on you, Young Darby. Please get your Quartz Journal for Lesson 3."

Seeing the Genie, I briefly consider whether to be honest or not and quickly decide in favor of it.

"Genie, I'm sorry, but I don't think *Happy School* is for me. I'm very upset today. I mean, I try to quarantine my WMDs, but there are too many unpleasant situations that over and over smack me in the face."

"Young Darby! We've only had two lessons. In fact, you will not experience the freedom I've promised until the very end of our ten lessons together. And even then, you will have to fight for your joy. Remember, the human brain is plastic,[30] which means it can change. Your sadness

---

30. Brain plasticity is a term that refers to the brain's ability to change and adapt.

is only minimally genetic. You can learn to forge new brain patterns by how you *intentionally* choose to think. You cannot judge the effectiveness of *Happy School* until you've been through all ten lessons.[31] By then you will have learned many beneficial strategies that will completely change how you think and, as a result, how you feel."[32]

I don't even try to argue. I know it's no use.

"It is of the utmost importance that you understand the foundational principles of *Happy School*," he says, "so I will review them again."[33]

Again? Isn't this review overkill?

"You've learned that your thoughts cause emotions," he says, "and that you can only think one thought at a time. You've learned that when WMDs descend, you can escape them and quarantine them by Playing Hot Potatoes and then by Moving into Another Room in Your Brain (thinking about something else)."

"I think I've got it," I say, letting him know I am not in elementary school.

He ignores my comment and continues. "You are to think about and problem-solve your WMDs in only one of the three times we discussed. You brainstorm and record Steps of Action to improve and correct your problems, if possible. And then you intentionally Reframe, Refute, or Replace each of your WMDs with more optimistic thinking."

Can we move on? I think to myself.

"Don't 'awfulize' your WMDs," he reminds me. "Your WMDs are neither *preferred nor wanted*, but they are not a catastrophe."

---

31. Of course, various brains have different degrees of negatively ingrained thinking habits or patterns. For example, those with PTSS will need more retraining and rebuilding than the protagonist in this book.

32. Those with prior brain injuries such as repeated concussions have a physical component that is not discussed in this book. Many studies are now seriously looking at some of the practices of contact sports such as tackle football. Many experts believe head injuries such as concussions from football injuries are harmful to children's brains, so please, parents, be cautious.

33. Be sure you understand these foundational principles since the material in *Happy School* is cumulative and builds on prior concepts. The summaries of the Genie's teachings are included at the back of this book. The concepts are relatively easy to understand but take years of practice to master. And mastery is your goal.

He's right. There is a lot of new information to learn. Maybe he should give me a break for a couple of weeks to practice this much info and then come back.

"Today we are going to learn a principle that again, when learned, can be life-changing as far as your thinking."

I wish he would quit calling everything *life-changing.*

"Life is *as you assign it,* Young Darby. This fact seems intuitively wrong, but it's true.[34] Events and situations *are only upsetting if you construe them to be.* That is because—whether you are aware of it or not—you are the one assigning an interpretation to every situation and circumstance."[35]

What is he saying now? More mumbo jumbo.

"Your happiness is relative to a scale *you've* created," he continues. "Your happiness does not depend on what happens to you as much as *what conclusions you make* when events occur. External circumstances only predict a tiny portion of your happiness. People with the exact same external circumstances assign different interpretations and thus feel vastly different about them. It's *how you think about your circumstances,* how you *interpret them,* that matters."

I certainly am going to need some help understanding *this* principle.

"Let's explore some events and situations and discuss the different ways one could choose to interpret them," he suggests.

Yes, definitely, let's.

"I will give you four examples, and you will then see how one assigns an interpretation to each circumstance in life," he says. "Example one is a woman who worked for a company for twenty years. The owners sold the company, and the woman was without a job."

"That's discouraging," I say.

"Is it? Remember, *it's only upsetting if you construe it to be.* Let's compare

---

34. Be sure your mind is bathed with biblical principles so you will know how to assign correct interpretations.

35. I am not talking about the fact that there is *objective morality.* There most definitely is. But there are a million situations in which assigning a value is helpful. Renewing your mind with biblical principles will train your mind how to think correctly.

how two different women might think about this situation. Woman A might say to herself, 'How dare they mistreat me like this. I'll never find another job like this one. No one wants to hire someone at my age.'"

That's what I would say to myself.

"But Woman B says to herself, 'This is not preferred, but there's no use feeling sorry for myself. I am older but wiser and have more experience. Surely someone would like to hire me. Not many people enjoy looking for work, but I will not waste another second on that thought. Instead, I will spruce up my resume and throw myself back into the fray. Who knows? *This may be the best thing that ever happened to my career.* I choose to believe there is opportunity in this obstacle.'"

"I can't imagine having the mindset or self-talk of Woman B," I say.

"You can train your mind to scan for the positive," the Genie says. "Let me give you another example. Let's suppose your child has some problems, either with behavior, learning, social skills, or even physical ailments."

I do hope I get perfect children someday. I guess all women wish for that.

"Woman A feels sorry for herself, resents the burden of her child's problems, and thinks how unfortunate she is."

That's how I would feel.

"However, Woman B knows that everyone has obstacles or difficult situations in their lives, and her needy child is one of hers. She decides to do everything in her power to take Herculean, massive action to help her child. She scans the universe for solutions to help her child and tells herself that she is doing everything humanly possible to help him.[36] She then tells herself that other women have had children with problems, and the ones with dogged perseverance often figure out how to solve those problems. Then she declares that she will be one of those."[37]

---

36. Not counting the power of prayer.
37. And always, with the power of God to do the impossible.

It sounds heroic to me to take Herculean action to help your child and not feel self-pity. Bravo for her, I think. "Woman B is impressive" is all I can mutter to the Genie.

"In example three," he says, "imagine a man that is waiting in line in a bank when a robbery occurs. He gets shot in the arm."

Oh, dear, must we discuss violent situations?

"Person A tells himself he was a victim, and it's unfair. He plays movies in his mind about how he could have avoided the shooting if he had simply first gotten gas for his car. He feels sorry for himself and says how horrible this shooting and the subsequent surgery, physical therapy, and lifelong limitations are. He tells himself that this has forever maimed him and changed his life for the worse."

I agree. Being shot sounds horrible, and it is unfair.

"Person B, on the other hand, not preferring to have been shot, says to himself, 'I'm so glad I didn't get killed. I will focus on being grateful that although this surgery means I will have some limitations, I will still have a host of pleasures in my life. I can still enjoy my life, even if this interruption was unwanted. I refuse to feel sorry for myself but will, instead, be grateful for what I still have.'"

Does anyone really think like that? I don't know anyone who does.

"For our last example, number four," he continues, "imagine a scenario where…"

I interrupt. "A scenario where the woman is approaching her mid-thirties, and there are no good husband prospects in sight."

Smiling, the Genie says, "Alright, let's discuss that example. Woman A says to herself, 'I've tried and failed, and now the good men are gone. I'm old and getting older, and the probability that I'm going to be forever alone looms larger and more certain.'"

I'm Woman A for sure.

"But Woman B tells herself, 'The past doesn't necessarily predict the future. I've learned a lot about relationships, and I can still take massive action to learn much more. Many women in their thirties find good men to marry. I must spend my time thinking about how to improve myself and how to meet great men. This is no time or place for self-pity or ruminating on past failure.'"

"How would I ever learn to be optimistic like that?" I ask the Genie.

"With practice," the Genie says. "But the huge takeaway from today's lesson is that you are creating your own emotional environment by your own interpretations. *It's only upsetting if you construe it to be.* You have the power to assign to situations the value you choose; that is, to write your own interpretations."

This would be extremely difficult for me. I see all glasses as half empty.

"To repeat, your happiness does not depend on what happens to you as much as what conclusions you make when events occur. It's how you think about your circumstances and how you interpret them that matter. It is shocking to most humans to learn that they can listen in on their interpretations of events (the Parade) and decide to choose a more positive and optimistic interpretation. It is critically important that you carefully assign positive interpretations to almost every event and situation."

He keeps saying basically the same thing—that my thinking, not my circumstances, is my problem.

"You see, everyone experiences adversity," he continues, "and you can choose to view adversity as possibly laden with opportunities. Within the obstacle,[38] there may be a better way forward. You can retrain yourself to think like this, to scan for the positive, and to insist there are opportunities and benefits buried within the obstacle."

"Opportunities? Benefits?" I say in disbelief.

"When faced with adversity, interrupt and refute your self-talk of self-pity, hopelessness, powerlessness, and coming devastation," he says. "Instead, command yourself to expect a glad surprise around the river bend. When you are tempted to think gloom and doom, Play Hot

---

38. In the Old Testament, Joseph was sold as a slave to Egyptian merchants. But this "obstacle" became an opportunity, and he became second in command in Egypt, thus saving his family of origin from starvation.

Potatoes, and choose to Move into Another Room in Your Brain. Choose courage, not self-pity. Often there are jewels hidden in adversity that were not previously available."

I don't think I can do this.

"You can say the obstacle is too big," he says, "or you can say the Creator hears, cares, and is able. Dismantle your current belief system of hopelessness because the Creator is able to do immeasurably more than all you ask or imagine."[39]

Maybe, but He probably won't for me.

"To review, Young Darby, you can't predict happiness by a person's life events but only by their beliefs about the events. As I said, when the same event happens to different people, they make very different conclusions about that event. People with the exact same life events end up with very different levels of life satisfaction. It's a matter of how they interpret events and how they talk to themselves."

He wants me to refute the dialog in my head that says things are awful. He wants me to consciously select facts to make myself feel fortunate (instead of having self-pity) and choose to believe something good will come of it.[40] I'm not sure I want to do this pie-in-the-sky assignment.

"Psychological stress comes from a negative perception of events, and now you know that you can assign value to every situation in your mind," he says.

It's going to take some time for me to process this. Like a lifetime.

"Your distress over Leland not marrying you, your pain over your mother's criticism, and your hatred of your job are all emotions produced in your mind by your *thoughts* about your circumstances, not the circumstances themselves," he says.

That's a mind-blowing and radical statement, and I'm certainly not willing to embrace that premise yet. In fact, I don't really even completely understand it.

---

39. Ephesians 3:20
40. "In all things God works for the good of those who love Him" (Romans 8:28 NIV).

"Your emotions don't reveal the quality of your life; they reveal *the interpretation you're giving your circumstances.* Disappointment is inevitable in life, but *discouragement* is optional because you get to assign an interpretation to every event and situation. It's time for you to get ready to meet your friend Ellie, so I will depart, but I will return soon." He evaporates before my eyes.

I'm still not sure I understand that it's only upsetting if I construe it to be. For example, let me see if I can process the thought that Shelby moving out is only upsetting because I construe it to be. Maybe I could look at this situation like this: Even though I'll lose the rent money, it's a chance to get rid of Shelby since her presence is annoying. Well, actually, that did present a glimmer of a good feeling. But still.

There's no hope for me to become happy until my other big problems change. The Genie's teaching is lofty—not practical—and difficult to comprehend.

I can't work in my Quartz Journal now since I have to meet Ellie, but I guess I could try later to apply some of the Genie's principles to my wretched life.

Pulling into the parking lot of the Vesta Home Show, I notice it is exceptionally crowded this year. Texting Ellie, we discover we parked only a few rows apart. After buying our tickets, we ride a shuttle to the new homes on display. Rounding a corner, the six houses in this year's show come into view. Mansions like these excite me, much like walking through the gates of the Magic Kingdom at Disney World when I was a child.

Ellie and I stand in line with the crowd to walk through the first two houses. We gush over the huge windows, state-of-the-art kitchens, marble columns, and twin winding staircases. While we're waiting in line to enter another house, I quickly catch up Ellie on the Leland disaster. Because I just thoroughly dissected the drama with Whitney a few hours earlier, I only give Ellie the highlights.

"Since I'm not marrying Leland," I say, "and since I hate my job to the moon and back, I've got to find some work I enjoy." Ellie has been an interior designer for six years and has pleaded with me to get back into the field. ("You have a natural knack for scale and color," she has repeatedly told me.) It's true that I do seem to have a proclivity for knowing what would look classic and beautiful, but to be a designer, I would need to learn so much more. Thinking of Ellie's beautiful posts on Instagram reminds me again how I have stupidly wasted the last ten years on the wrong men instead of working on a career.

"You could either go back to graduate school for interior design or," she pauses, "as I've also suggested to you before, you could pursue your love of cooking."

"I know, I know," I say. Ellie knows me well and knows those are my top two interests.

As Ellie and I enter the third house, I already know this one will be my favorite. The foyer is magnificent with marble floors and a wide-open layout. There is a gigantic kitchen in the back, and huge windows flank the entire rear of the house, showcasing the backyard's pool area and outdoor kitchen. The beauty of the architecture as well as the exquisite furnishings completely captures and absorbs my mind.

While surveying the high ceilings, I see a woman I recognize across the room. I think it's Maggie Stenson. Maggie mentored a group of my sorority sisters when I was in college. I haven't talked to her for at least twelve years. Even though she was involved with several civic and business activities back then, she still made time to meet weekly with a few of us who definitely needed to mature emotionally and spiritually.

Telling Ellie I'll be right back, I walk up behind Maggie.

"Maggie?" I ask. "Do you remember me?"

"Darby McChesney!" she says as she reaches forward to hug me. "Why, I would never forget you. Great to see you! How long has it been?" Her eyes may have a few more wrinkles than they did twelve years ago, but they still sparkle with sincerity and energy.

"What are you doing these days?" she asks, obviously glad to see me and sincerely interested. That's Maggie, though. I decide to be a little more honest than usual.

"I'm hanging in there. My boyfriend and I just broke up, so that's always an abrupt change in direction," I say with a little laugh to pretend I don't care. "And actually, I'm in a bad job, so I'm thinking hard about what I'm going to do next, whether to pursue interior design again or pursue being a professional chef."

Ugh, I think. The woman hasn't seen me in twelve years, and I've just poured out my troubles like I'm in a psychiatrist's office.

"I remember that you were interested in interior design," she says with no judgment whatsoever. "But I didn't know you liked to cook. My hunch is that you'll be good at whatever you decide to pursue." Maggie was never short on encouragement.

"What about you?" I ask. "What are you up to?"

"My husband passed away five years ago," she says solemnly. "But after I got back on my feet, I bought an old house in Midtown and remodeled it. I opened a business similar to a bed-and-breakfast, something I've wanted to do for years."

"In what way is your business like a bed-and-breakfast?" I ask.

"My customers are business people who travel and want a more home-like environment with fresh cooked dinners *at night*. So I'm open Sunday night through Friday morning and serve dinner five nights. Rather unusual business model, I know," she says.

Before I ask more questions, a tall man walks up to us. His blue eyes are strong and piercing, and he has thick eyebrows and a defined nose. His hair is a little long, very dark, and a bit wavy. He's on the lean side but with definition. I feel a catch and flip in my stomach.

"Darby, this is my nephew, Peter Needleman. He moved to Memphis a couple years ago to help me with some of my real estate ventures."

"Nice to meet you, Darby," he says. He's not in a hurry and has a calm, controlled energy.

Somehow I squeak out, "Nice to meet you." I always get tongue-tied around men who are this handsome. Even in the presence of this Romeo,

I remember that when Maggie was meeting with us, she used to frequently talk about her sister in Oregon.

"So this is your Oregon sister's son?" I wonder aloud.

"You have a great memory, Darby," she says, impressed. "My sister died of breast cancer four years ago."

"I'm sorry to hear that," I say. Quickly turning to Peter, I add, "And your mom." At that moment, it strikes me that Maggie has endured the loss of her husband and her sister in the last few years.

Changing the subject, Peter asks, "How do you two know each other?"

"I mentored a group of college sorority girls around twelve years ago," Maggie says, smiling, "and Darby was one of my favorites."

Why did she have to tell him it was twelve years ago? Now he knows I'm in my thirties. But my wrinkles probably already told him that.

"Aunt Maggie can spin ten plates at once, so it doesn't surprise me," he says with a straight look on his face.

"Yes, maybe even twenty plates," I say. Such a stupid thing to say. Gosh, really? Twenty plates? I need to work on my small talk skills.

Maggie directs her next comment to Peter. "Darby is looking for work. She is interested in interior design or cooking."

Peter changes his gaze from Maggie to me. "What are you doing now?"

I hate this question. How do I answer? I blunder and stumble as I explain, "Well, I am now working in a law firm, but I... I... don't like it. So I've got to find some work I enjoy."

Peter's voice sounds like he could be a broadcaster on Sunday Night Football. I'd like to glance down to see if he has on a wedding ring, but I dare not get caught doing that.

"What kind of cooking do you do?" Maggie asks. People don't usually ask me this many questions, so I'm surprised, but of course, I enjoy talking about myself.

"I love all kinds," I say, "but my current favorite is finding different healthy cuisines from around the world. I insist on using fresh and organic ingredients," I say, laughing a little in case they don't realize how important wholesome food is.

Maggie raises her eyebrows and looks inquisitively at Peter. I have no idea what her gesture means. He responds to her facial gestures but with a very stoic face. He would definitely be a hard one to figure out.

Maggie turns to me again and says in a serious voice, "Darby, I am currently looking for a cook for my guests. It may not be what you're looking for as I would only need you from 4:00 p.m. to 8:00 p.m. Sunday through Thursday nights. But actually, you could work an additional four hours on either Saturday or Sunday to plan menus and shop. But that's only a total of twenty-four hours. Would you be interested in talking about it?"

Cooking? Getting paid to cook? Even though it's only twenty-four hours, I don't hesitate. "Yes, I'm definitely interested!" Even though the money will not be enough to support me, I can continue to use some of my dad's inheritance until I figure things out. My thoughts are whirling. Why, I could go back to school during the day and work in the evenings for Maggie. I'm already excited over the possibility.

"Why don't I call you later this afternoon, and we'll talk more about it," she says, and we exchange contact info. Although she probably doesn't pay much, I've got to find a way to get away from toxic Jana, even if it's just a refuge until I can figure things out.

"We're planning a wedding," she says as she looks at Peter, "and the reception is going to be at my house, so I'm up to my neck in work. I could sure use some help with cooking for my weekly guests."

"That's a big undertaking," I say, "having a wedding reception at your house."

She looks at Peter again, "Yes, but I would do anything for my sister's children."

Oh well, so much for Peter being available. But that's okay, because when men are that good looking, they are usually full of themselves.

We say goodbye, and I find Ellie.

"Whoa, who was that lady, and who was that hunk?" Ellie asks.

"That was Maggie Stenson, my college mentor, and her nephew who, by the way, is getting married. But she owns a bed-and-breakfast, and we're going to talk this afternoon about my cooking for her guests at night."

"A job cooking? Now that should be a step up from working for that monstrous boss of yours," she says. Then she adds sadly, "But it's too bad that fine-looking specimen is off the market."

My thoughts exactly. But then I also remember that at my age, all the good ones are gone. Ellie and I finish all six houses, which I thoroughly enjoy, but in the back of my mind, I keep thinking about quitting mean Jana and cooking for Maggie. It will be a temporary respite, and I'll have time to figure out what work I want to pursue. A little breather seems to be in sight.

Before going home, I make my regular visit to see Nana, my paternal grandmother. My grandfather, Papa, died when I was sixteen but not before making a huge impact on me. I think back to my childhood and how I loved to spend the night with them in their tiny little two-bedroom house. Nana and Papa didn't have much money, but they certainly knew how to enjoy life. They loved fishing, playing cards, smoking cigarettes (my mother had a fit about that), and baking fresh bread and cookies. On Halloween, Nana made elaborate witches on her front porch that were connected to a vacuum hose. Then, from inside her house, she talked through the hose like a witch and scared the trick-or-treaters out of their minds. Nana and I used to laugh so hard that we cried. We would stay up late, play Canasta, and eat snickerdoodles.

My mother never approved of Nana and Papa's income, and she blamed them for Dad not having more ambition to grind out a living in corporate America. And of course, she hated their cigarette smoking (which I agree was unhealthy, but they refused to give it up). Mom never wanted Bailey to spend time at their house, so it was always just me. No wonder I was clearly the favorite grandchild.

Nana is now ninety. Repeatedly, she has told me she doesn't ever want to leave her apartment, if possible, but finish her years right there.

Nana has hired housekeepers over the years to help with the housecleaning, but now she is unable to do anything. When Nana needed a Power of Attorney, it was no surprise that she asked me. Immediately, I had access to her financial situation. She is worth well over a million dollars! Of course, she lived so frugally that no one knew. I still have not told my mother since she would work night and day to see how she could get her hands on some of that money. Nana is leaving 50 percent of her money to me, 25 percent to Bailey, and 25 percent to her church of forty years. There's going to be a big blowup someday when that will is read.

One of my ongoing battles with Bailey and my mom is that they badger me to put Nana in a nursing home instead of paying for caregivers to come to her house. "She's demented and like a vegetable," my mother once said. "She won't even know."

"But I'll know," I responded, always finding courage to stand up to my mom if it involved Nana. "She asked to stay in her own apartment as long as she could afford it, so I'm going to see that she does," I said.

"Tell me how much money she has, Darby," my mother demanded.

"I'm sorry, but Nana asked me to keep her financial affairs confidential."

"You're stubborn like your father," my mom said. "And stupid—stupid to waste money on old people who don't even know their own name."

My disgust rises again as I remember this conversation. I think of my grandmother's tenderness and generosity in contrast to the selfish, greedy schemes of my mom.

Walking into Nana's house, I greet Ernestine, one of Nana's caregivers. Nana is eating a bowl of vegetable beef soup that Ernestine prepared from scratch.

"Hi, Darby," Ernestine says. "Would you like a bowl of soup?"

"No thanks," I say, smiling, "but it smells wonderful. How is Nana?"

"About the same," she says.

I walk over to Nana, who is staring out the window. "Nana, it's me, Darby," I say. "Do you know me?"

She turns and with a blank stare, says, "No, who are you?"

"I'm your granddaughter," I say.

"I'm sorry, but I don't know you," and she turns back to look out the window. Ernestine and I exchange glances as we know Nana is slipping away.

My heart aches, but I know there is an expiration on life for all of us, and Nana, at ninety, is approaching hers.

"I brought some body lotion," I say. "Let me rub some on your arms and hands." Having a mini-massage is always one of Nana's favorite treats.

"Oh my! Thank you so much. What did you say your name was?" she asks.

"Darby. I'm your granddaughter."

She smiles and turns to me so I can start massaging the lotion into her skin. I start singing old hymns to Nana, and she joins in. We sing "The Old Rugged Cross" and "I Come to the Garden Alone." She knows every word and seems to enjoy the singing as much as the massage.

In about thirty minutes, Nana falls asleep in her chair. As she sleeps, I kiss her cheek, and it almost makes me cry. One of the few people who ever truly loved me unconditionally is slipping away into eternity. I feel more alone than ever.

I chat with Ernestine a little about Nana's meds and schedule and then leave. A sadness fills me as I back out of the driveway, thinking about the care she gave me as a child. Then I think about how I want to be a grandmother like Nana someday. But then the thought that I'll never even have children, much less grandchildren, makes me start to spiral down. Here I go again, watching my main WMD rear its ugly head from nowhere. How often situations arise that lead me to ruminate about my WMDs. I play Hot Potatoes and decide to Move into Another Room in My Brain. I shift to thinking about my possible new job with Maggie.

When I get home, I notice my Tory Burch shoes have arrived. I know I should send them back since I have no husband in sight, no roommate to help pay my rent, and an income that's about to drop. But the shoes are so cute! I think about how to justify keeping them.

Maggie is not supposed to call for another ten minutes, so I relax a little and check my phone. There are two text messages, and both are from girls in my Sorority Supper Club.

"Sorry to hear that you and Leland broke up. Are you okay?" one text message reads.

Another one says, "I'm checking on you. Just found out you and Leland broke up. I'm surprised that Leland is dating Bethany, though. Can you talk?"

How does everyone suddenly know about the breakup? And even more that he and Bethany are seeing each other? I'm bewildered. It just happened on Wednesday, and this is Saturday.

While waiting for Maggie to call, I check Instagram. What I see feels like I'm being thrown over the rail of a second-story balcony. Bethany has posted a picture of herself and Leland eating ribs at the Rendezvous Restaurant. Her caption is this: "Great ribs. Great night." I actually feel nauseous. How embarrassing that Leland has moved on so fast and with one of my so-called friends!

What a jerk Leland is. He never had money or energy to take me out, but now he takes out The Girls three times in four days. My thoughts are spinning, and I have no idea how to handle this humiliation. Another text message appears from a third friend in the monthly Sorority Supper Club. "Just found out about you and Leland. I'm really sorry. Call to chat when you can."

Sure, that's want I want to do, call all three of those friends and tell them that loser Darby is alone again, and this time The Girls have stolen him. Right. I want to talk about that scenario. My stomach is in complete knots, and I have no idea what to do or think.

My phone rings, and it's Maggie. I had almost forgotten about my telephone appointment. I wonder if this cooking gig will work out. Nothing else in my life does.

After some pleasant introductory talk, Maggie suggests, "What about coming over tomorrow and trying out the job? We can see if we are a good fit. I'll pay you twenty-five dollars an hour."

Even though I make substantially more than that right now, my current high hourly wage is paired with a prison warden.

"That would be great," I say.

"I've got five guests registered for tomorrow night, so that's seven people you'll cook for," she says.

"Seven? Five guests and you make six," I say, helping Maggie with her math.

"Peter lives in the in-law suite in my backyard, and I feed him most nights," she says. "Benefits of being my sister's child," she adds, laughing.

I wonder where Peter's fiancée is, but I'm sure I'll figure that out soon enough.

"What are we cooking?" I ask.

"I thought maybe I'd let you decide that. Either I can shop for the ingredients tomorrow," she pauses and adds, "or even better, you can."

Tomorrow is Sunday, and after church I have no plans since my social life rates minus three on a scale of one to ten.

"I would be happy to plan and shop," I say. "I'll text you my menu and grocery list in an hour, and you can tell me what ingredients you already have."

Hanging up, I think this is definitely one good thing in an ocean full of sorrows. The sorrows still outweigh the good things nine to one, but for one moment, a feeling of something new, something positive, warms me. Cooking for Maggie will give me something productive and positive to think about and do. This is a small step forward, and I feel the tiniest bit better, even with all my friends whispering about Leland and The Girls behind my back.

Answering all my text messages the best I can to save face, I then pour myself a glass of wine and reopen the box with my Tory Burch shoes. Wow! They are super cute. Do I dare keep them with my finances in such a wad?

My mother has now called three times, and I've declined them all. I text her back that I'll call her soon with some good news.

She texts back, "Did Leland come back? I'd be surprised, but I can't think of what else good could have happened to you."

My mother. My critical, negative, neurotic mother. What do I do with her? What do I do with paying this rent by myself? What do I do with all my friends talking behind my back? And what do I do about being ancient and having deteriorating eggs? The dark cloud comes closer as I list my WMDs.

But aha! I remember! I have a strategy when the WMDs begin to press in. I will Move into Another Room in My Brain by working on my menu for tomorrow night. Now there's a subject I like. I can actually feel my mood rise just thinking about planning an interesting menu. Maybe I'll consider going to cooking school and getting certified. Moving into Another Room in My Brain is a pretty good idea, I admit to myself. It may be small, but at least it gives me a degree of control over my mood.

After planning the menu, I text Maggie. How quickly the time went by. Waiting for Maggie to text back, I decide to pour myself a second glass of wine. I know this much wine couldn't be good for me. I'll have to deal with that another day.

Lesson 4

The Urgent Necessity of Stopping Bad Habits (and How to Do It)

Sunday, August 26

Since Leland rarely attended church with me, I am accustomed to going by myself. I need to write that fact down in my Quartz Journal under the WMD that Leland and I broke up. Clearly, I now see I was settling with Leland in so many ways because I was, well, desperate.

Now I know better than to let my mind go down the path of how old I am, how few good men there are, how Leland wasted two years of my life, yada yada, poor me. It's so subtle how those WMD thoughts creep up and I don't even recognize them. Learning new and better self-talk and especially Moving into Another Room in my Brain has been a big help to me. I get to choose how I frame external circumstances. If I "walk by sight" and tell myself that it's over for me and that I'm a confirmed spinster, I feel discouraged. But I can choose to tell myself that there's still hope.[41] I will myself to choose hope while I Move into Another Room in My Brain. What should I think about now? I'll think about cooking for Maggie.

---

41. He hears, He cares, He is able.

Gathering all my groceries and supplies, I put Maggie's address in my GPS and head that direction. Pulling into her driveway, I notice that the large, stucco house perfectly reflects Maggie. The European architecture is stately, and the huge oak trees in the neighborhood give it the feel of aristocracy. Maggie's front yard is full of rose bushes, crepe myrtles, impatiens, and petunias.

Parking in the back, I carry the groceries into the kitchen. On the way inside, I see Peter walking out of his in-law suite. "Need some help?" he offers.

"Sure, thanks," I say, already feeling tongue-tied. As he approaches, I feel almost frozen by his smell, his face, and those blue eyes. It's all too much. He's got that strong, controlled personality that soothes a wreck like me.

"Since I'm helping to carry in the groceries," he says matter-of-factly and with no facial expression whatsoever, "I will expect seconds tonight."

"Let's hope you want seconds," I say, attempting to joke. Again, so stupid of me. Why can't I ever think of anything clever to say?

Maggie walks out the back door to help, too. "Darby! Welcome! I've been so relaxed all day since I didn't have to plan, shop, or cook dinner. I'm very happy to try this arrangement. I'll be your assistant tonight until you find your way around my kitchen."

Unloading the groceries, I go into focused concentration. I'm making shaved steak with chimichurri sauce for an entrée, so I slice the meat. Then I season the squash, cabbage, and red bell peppers with cumin, coriander, and an oregano spice blend. Fortunately, Maggie has large, modern ovens and updated countertops for prepping. She has a huge warming oven and a gigantic fridge. I feel like I'm in a restaurant kitchen.

At home before I came, I made the salad dressing, prepped the sauce, and combined the seasonings for the meat.

"My goodness, I wasn't expecting you to prep and work before you got here," she says, obviously impressed with my organization.

"It didn't take long, and I know things take longer the first time," I say.

"This is how I remember you, Darby, always bringing more than your share to the table." That was a nice thing to say. What a contrast to the way my mother criticizes everything I do.

Maggie's kitchen has a huge bay window that looks out into a gorgeous backyard with a direct view of the in-law suite. I'm not paying serious attention because I'm so focused on my work, but I do notice when a car drives up and a girl with a long, blonde ponytail gets out. This must be Peter's fiancée. She and Peter talk for a moment, and then she comes into the kitchen through the back door.

Maggie greets her warmly. "Darby, this is Cassie, our upcoming bride."

"Nice to meet you," I say, as friendly as I know how. Cassie seems distracted and very uninterested in me. But what should I expect when I am merely the hired help?

"Hey," she says quickly and then turns her attention to Maggie.

"I thought I'd show you the wedding invitations," she says excitedly to Maggie.

I'm pretty good at reading people, and I can sense Maggie's ambivalence between wanting to be available to Cassie and her prior commitment to help me in the kitchen.

"I'd love to see the invitations," she says. "Let me wash my hands and look at them a minute. My guests will be down for dinner at 6:30, and I need to help Darby as this is her first day. I can look at them more carefully after dinner."

If Cassie was tuned in, she would know that Maggie is busy. But Cassie doesn't pause a bit. Within seconds, she has the box on the table, the top is off, and she's waiting for Maggie to gush over her invitations. I'm wondering if I smell the scent of a bridezilla.

Maggie makes the appropriate raves over the invitations, and then Cassie proceeds to talk about which pens to use to address the invitations when they need to go out. Just by listening in a little, I understand now that Maggie is addressing the invitations. No wonder Cassie is going into such detail.

"Can I put them in the pantry and talk about them later?" Maggie sweetly asks. "My guests will be here shortly, and as I said, this is Darby's first day, so I need to help her."

Cassie starts gathering all the supplies she had put on the table and is somewhat miffed that she must wait.

"Okay," Cassie says, with slight annoyance. "I'm meeting some girl-friends for dinner tonight, so I'll be back tomorrow. When do you think you can start addressing the invitations? There are 300, and I'd like them to go out this Friday."

Wow! Now I know for sure Peter is marrying a bridezilla. How do these high-maintenance wenches get these amazing guys? It always astounds me. Can't he see the trouble he's getting into? She's spoiled to the core. I think about how hard I tried to be a good girlfriend to Leland and the way it got me nothing but the axe. But here's this little self-absorbed princess throwing herself around, and she gets the grand prize, Peter Needleman. It all seems so unfair.

Glancing at the clock, I see that it's 6:00, so I need to step it up. I can't give another thought to Peter's bridezilla fiancée.

Maggie's guests start arriving, and I can hear her as she welcomes them, showing them their rooms. But I'm watching the clock and the heat on the stove, paying attention to when everything will be done.

Maggie's guests come down for dinner right at 6:30. Usually her guests go through a buffet line, but tonight I have plated the food. I walk into the dining room and serve each guest separately.

Retreating to the kitchen, I hear the oohs and the aahs begin. "How delicious this salad is, Maggie!"

"My! What is in this sauce?"

"This is superb, Maggie."

I walk back into the dining room to refill water glasses, and Peter notices me. "This is Darby's first night as the cook, everyone. I'll rate it as…well…fair."

Everyone laughs and knows Peter is teasing me. Everyone has been complimenting the food throughout the entire meal.

"This is one of the best meals I've had all year," says one middle-aged man.

Another woman comments, "Just marvelous. You are a wonderful cook, young lady!"

Peter jumps back in the conversation. "Okay, okay, it was pretty good, I admit. Aunt Maggie, now I'm wondering if you've charged these folks enough since you have this talented chef."

Again, all the guests laugh and beg her not to but agree she could. The friendly crowd's banter could not be more encouraging.

Some of Maggie's guests go to their rooms, and a couple men move to the living room to drink coffee. The raves over the meal are still echoing in my head.

Maggie is scurrying around making sure the doors are locked, her guests are comfortable, and the lights are turned down. I'm in the kitchen cleaning up when Peter walks through on his way out the back door. "Are you a one-trick pony, or do you have any other five-star meals in your pocket?" he asks, again with no expression on his face.

"That's all I've got," I say. "Tomorrow it's hot dogs and French fries." Finally, I say something decent.

His face shows a hint of amusement. "I might finally gain some weight if I eat like this all the time." Peter is on the lean side, so I understand that he probably struggles to keep weight on.

"Did you like cooking here tonight?" he asks. He's such a nice guy, taking time to talk to other people about their interests.

Maggie walks in and hears his question. "I'd like to hear the answer to that question, too," she says.

"I *loved* being here. I really loved it," I say, trailing off.

"But," Maggie says and pauses, "it's not enough hours, is it?"

"Well," I say, pondering my answer, "it's not. So I'll have to figure out if I can make it work financially." I'm quitting Jana for sure tomorrow, but I'm not ready to tell that to Maggie.

"What if I threw in a room?" Maggie says in an instant. Before I can say a word, she adds, "I mean, what if you lived here? I've got six rooms upstairs, and only five are usually booked for my guests. Could you make it work financially if you moved in here and didn't have to pay rent or utilities somewhere else? I've got Wi-Fi, too."

I am totally caught off-guard with this offer. I mean, I've only cooked for Maggie one night, and she's offering me a room in her house? We did have a special relationship when she mentored our group in college. And I do think I am capable of doing an excellent job cooking for her guests. But my first thought is that I can't because it's all too fast. Actually, I don't need more than a room and a bathroom since I would have access to Maggie's kitchen. And this would present an opportunity to do something wildly different.

"Don't give her the green room, Aunt Maggie," Peter says very seriously, interrupting my thought process, "because you know I like to go in there and watch that big screen TV."

Maggie laughs, knowing Peter's sense of humor. "Sorry, Peter. You'll have to watch TV downstairs if we can persuade Darby to move in."

With reluctance in his tone, he adds, "Well, I hope the food continues to be as good as tonight to compensate for the loss of my green room privileges," he says, shaking his head like he's making a big concession.

Peter is funny. I really like him. I really, really like him. At least we'll be friends. I won't be friends with his bridezilla, though, I can promise that.

"Let me think about it, but it does sound rather enticing," I say, already remembering a couple I know who needs an apartment and might be able to sublease mine.

Maggie hugs me and says, "Tonight I thought how I've missed you. You've always been a giver."

Driving home, I think about what Maggie said, that I'm a giver. I'd like to be a giver (versus a taker), but I often feel like I'm caught in the quicksand of my discouragement and negative emotions. I do try hard, though. I really do.

Walking into my apartment, I see the Genie sitting on the kitchen counter waiting for me. Actually, I'm in a decent mood, unlike most times when he shows up.

"I brought you some Babylonian figs," he says, handing me one. "Let's begin tonight's important lesson," he says.

There he goes again, saying how everything is important.

"Tonight I will teach you the urgent necessity of stopping bad habits," he says.

Sure. This guy has answers to self-control, one of the most confounding issues of all humanity.

"As you know, there are many harmful habits such as eating excess sugar and junk food, smoking, drinking excess alcohol, viewing porn, playing excessive video games, excess gambling, overspending, abusing recreational drugs or prescription drugs, and many others," he says.

I would have to confess to one or more of those bad habits.

"Bad habits are indulged in because of one of two—and only two—reasons," he says. "It's for pleasure or for dialing down emotional disturbance."

Surely there are other reasons.

"Bad habits are an easy way to find immediate pleasure," he says. "And likewise, they are effective in immediately dialing down unpleasant emotions such as anxiety, boredom, restlessness, annoyance, anger, resentment, self-pity, loneliness, failure, regret, guilt, grief, or any other unwanted emotion."

Admittedly, I do like escaping everything on that list.

"Therefore, in a way, bad habits *are* a solution," he says, "and they do actually offer an effective mechanism to immediately relax the brain, soften life from the unwanted, and fill a void."

Immediately being the key word.

"Bad habits are truly the fastest way to hide from the harshness of life," he adds, "and create instant color and zest in one's life."

Very true.

"As you well know, your bad-habit-of-choice temporarily soothes, relieves, and dulls problems. It hides and blocks stress, overcomes boredom, and adds pleasure," he continues as though he's selling the benefits of bad habits. "Bad habits are often seen as a friend because they celebrate with you, relieve your boredom, and dispel your loneliness. In that way, giving them up seems like you're sacrificing something important."

He does get this.

"But bad habits are actually a con job because they only *temporarily* mask pain and in their wake leave *more* angst and pain," he explains. "Bad habits are more like a friend who is poisoning your coffee, stealing from your bank account, or sleeping with your boyfriend. Yes, they are powerful because they offer immediate relief and provide excitement, but they soon have you locked in a cage. Bad habits lie when they promise pleasure without negative consequences. But there are always negative consequences."

I should have known where he was going with this.

"Your bad habits are only a temporary solution to escaping and numbing unfulfilling relationships, unfulfilled dreams, unfulfilled longings, and chronic dissatisfaction and disappointment," he says.

Which is a perfect description of my life.

"Self-discipline will always lead to long-term benefits, and self-indulgence will always lead to long-term detriments," he continues. "But the key word is *long-term*. In the short term, self-indulgence is easier and more enjoyable, and the unschooled get sabotaged."

I'm not willing to call it a prison, but it's true that I can't seem to stop my spending, wine drinking, or indulging in huge amounts of screen time.

"Humans' own worst enemy of happiness is often themselves," he says. "They need to get out of their own way. They need to get clear on what they are doing that is harmful and self-destructive and stop doing it."

Uh, right. Just stop doing it. Sure. That's such dumb advice. No one would have bad habits if we could simply do that.

"I have presented Lessons 1 through 3 first, Young Darby, so you will have already discovered the magnificence of the truth that you can choose and control your thoughts. You can watch the Parade that Marches across Your Brain, Play Hot Potatoes, choose to Move into Another Room in Your Brain, and Assign a More Optimistic Interpretation to an External Event. These are powerful and life-changing skills to know before we tackle today's lesson, *The Urgent Necessity of Stopping Bad Habits (and How to Do it)*."

I especially need to address my little wine habit.

"Before you can move on to other principles in *Happy School*, you must stop your self-destructive habits," he says. "Any kind of addiction will imprison you so you cannot think correctly. You cannot be indulging in harmful behavior and expect to be happy. Continuing in bad habits against your own better judgment is a certain recipe for self-hate and despair."[42]

If I could stop, I would have already done so. I've tried. My life is just too crummy to handle without mood changers.

"Few things cause more emotional turmoil in one's brain than continuing bad habits against one's own better judgment," he says again. "If you make rules for yourself and break them, it is evidence that you have a problem in that area—whether it is food, cigarettes, alcohol, marijuana, shopping, or watching endless *YouTube* videos. Self-discipline is making rules for yourself and then following them."

I know. I know.

"Invoking self-discipline often seems to the untrained that they're missing out on legitimate pleasure," he continues.

Correct. FOMO. I often think how wine is a beautiful, life-affirming gift, so why should I abstain?

"Genie, I drink wine at night because, well, because it numbs me from all the disappointment in my life," I confess. There. I said it.

"Yes, I know you do," he says, "but tonight I am going to teach you how to stop that."

---

42. "He who neglects discipline despises himself" (Proverbs 15:32 NASB).

I think he's showing he's crazy right now. I mean, of course it is preferable if I stop. But how? *How? How* is the million-dollar question.

"I've tried!" I say. "I've tried to stop drinking, and then I slip up and give in again." I say that and then feel badly that I am admitting such a huge weakness.

I go on. "Genie, no one has the answers to self-discipline and self-mastery. Addiction is a genetic predisposition. A person is engineered that way or not, similar to having blue eyes or not." Sadly, I think that leaves me to be eaten alive by wolves because both my parents had (or have) low self-control.

"Young Darby, it amazes me where you come up with these false beliefs," he says, shaking his head. "Why, the human spirit can conquer almost anything, and certainly it can conquer bad habits and addictions. You can develop self-discipline and almost become an entirely different person. As you would expect, it's your thinking again that is the problem."

I try to be polite, but he's wrong. Dead wrong. "Alcohol is an addiction,[43] and that means it's virtually impossible to resist."[44]

"Obviously, I'm not saying an alcohol addiction or any addiction is easy to conquer, as the recovery and relapse rates demonstrate," he says. "But many people do recover forever, and I will teach you how you can be one of those people."

Sure. This cartoon character has answers millions of earthlings are looking for.

"To begin, let me remind you of the struggle that humans have in their own brains," he says. "Their Lower Self *pleads* for immediate pleasure and self-soothing against the better judgment of their Higher Self that *whispers* for long-term goals."

---

43. If you have an addiction, this is your first priority, and you need to educate yourself in every way possible so you can withdraw.

44. I'm not trying to downplay addiction. And if you are severely addicted to drugs or alcohol, please get medical care to withdraw. But most people can get through a few days of unpleasant symptoms of withdrawal. The same is true with cigarettes, sugar, and other addictions.

The *pleading* of my Lower Self versus the *whispering* of my Higher Self. Exactly.

"One brain lobe, which houses your Lower Self, is interested in immediate gratification," he explains. "But you also have another brain lobe that is interested in your long-term goals, housing your Higher Self. When they compete with each other, you have *cognitive dissonance*. That explains the battle you experience inside your brain, creating much of your current anguish."

It's true that I have two dueling selves inside of me.[45]

Humans have an unimaginable consciousness[46] that, when properly trained, can choose against their Lower Self," he says.

"Whatever I've done in the past hasn't worked, Genie. I'm afraid I'm a helpless victim of my Lower Self."

"You are anything but a victim," he says. "That is a false mindset. You definitely can overcome your Lower Self and consistently choose your Higher Self for your long-term benefit."

I'll believe it when I see it.

"What I've discovered in dealing with humans," he says, "is that they can usually accurately articulate the harm of continuing in their bad habits."

Yes, big debt from overspending, poisoning my health with alcohol, and less productivity from too much screen time—all of my bad habits are self-destructive, but I persist. That's why I'm crazy. I'm bipolar or narcissistic or some other psychological sickness.

"This is weird, Genie, because I do know the detriments of my bad habits, but I still continue. Isn't this a sign of mental illness?"

Laughing, he answers, "It absolutely is *not* a sign of mental illness. It is a sign that you have not been instructed properly on how to think and control your thoughts. Bad habits and addictions happen slowly. You did not willingly sign up to be enslaved by bad habits, but because of their

---

45. The Apostle Paul discusses these two selves in Romans 7.
46. This is because humans are made in the image of their Creator.

effectiveness in easing and softening 'the unwanted,' they dug grooves in your brain as 'solutions.' Now you must make new grooves."

I was definitely not warned.

"Many people go a lifetime without winning the battle over their Lower Self," he says. "A victory over your Lower Self—your desire for immediate gratification—will completely change your life. Overcoming your Lower Self's schemes will skyrocket your sense of dignity and self-esteem. To be happy, you must remove the disagreement inside your mind and conquer your Lower Self."

"So how in the world would I ever do that?" I ask.

"There are six simple steps to developing self-discipline in an area," he says. "Pick one bad habit that you'd like to overcome."

"I'd like to stop drinking two glasses of wine every night," I say. (Or maybe three, but what's the difference?)

"The steps to overcoming a temptation (one in which you have a craving or experience a cue) will become almost automatic with practice. But to explain the process, I must break it down into tiny steps," he says. "It will seem tedious at first to slowly go through each step, but it is of utmost importance."

I'm listening.

"Here is a list of the six steps."

He twirls his hand in the air, and my Quartz Journal appears with the following list—List 2—already written:

1. Write out the Detriments of Continuing and the Benefits of Stopping your bad habit.
2. Write out a proclamation of My Best Sane Higher Self.
3. Write out the arguments your Lower Self will use to ambush you and entice you to not follow your Best Sane Higher Self proclamation.
4. Write out how you will talk back to your Lower Self with your Best Sane Higher Self proclamation.

5. Be smoke, and let the dart of the craving pass through (to be explained).

6. Make a list of what topics you will think about (Rooms to Move Into) or Alternate Activities to Do (instead of your bad habit when you need to self-soothe and entertain.)

The Genie is correct that I have no idea what most of that means, so I hope he explains it all well.

"Step one," he says, "is to know the Detriments of Continuing and the Benefits of Stopping your bad habit. Please turn to this page in your Quartz Journal, and begin your lists of *reasons*. List reasons that convince your mind that your habit is hugely detrimental to your health, your finances, or your relationships."

On the page titled Detriments of Continuing and Benefits of Stopping, I see two columns, so I begin to list reasons. Under Detriments of Continuing, I write, *Excessive alcohol harms my immune system, causes cancer, dehydrates my skin, depresses my mood, and makes me feel crummy the next morning.* And then under Benefits of Stopping, I write, *My health would improve at the cellular level, my skin would improve, my productivity would increase, and my waist would get smaller.* I can easily list these since I have wrestled with my nightly alcohol habit for the last ten years.

"Having powerful and compelling reasons is always the first key to changing habits," he says. "Until you desperately want something, you will not have the motivation to do something different."

"In my sane moments, Genie, I really know it's best to stop," I say. "But I get hijacked every night."

"Yes, I understand," he says, "and these six steps are your strategy to overcome that."

That's pretty arrogant to assert. I've already read several books on stopping, as well as listened to several podcasts.

"Now you are ready for step two," he says. "After reviewing the detriments and benefits you listed, title a page in your Quartz Journal *Proclamation of My Best Sane Higher Self.* Write out what your Best Sane

Higher Self wants in moments of complete sanity (versus in the under-tow of your craving or addiction)."

It's annoying how he always wants me to write everything out. Is this really necessary?

"Life is short, and the hour glass is ticking," he says, "so therefore you want to live your Best Sane Higher Life, Young Darby. You want to pursue your dreams, your goals, and your vision. You want deep, meaningful relationships. You want a healthy mental mindset and a healthy body. And as you know, your bad habit robs you of many of these."

He's right. I admit it. I've tried moderating my wine intake umpteen times, and that doesn't seem to ever work. I know the only thing to do is abstain. But how? *How?* I decide to comply for now and begin writing.

On the page titled Proclamation of My Best Sane Higher Self, I write, *Because of the detriments and benefit lists, it is hugely obvious to me that when I'm in my Best Sane Higher Self state of mind, it is clear that I should abstain from all alcohol at all times in order to pursue my best life, my dreams, my goals, and more.*[47]

He doesn't comment on my proclamation but merely continues. "Step three is to be ready for an ambush. You must know that a battle is coming in which your Lower Self will suggest reasons why you should *not* follow your Best Sane Higher Self proclamation. Therefore, title a new page in your Quartz Journal, Reasons My Lower Self Uses to Ambush Me."

Yes, ambush is totally the right word.

"Write down every reason you can think of that your Lower Self uses to entice you to participate in your bad habit," he says. "You will actually add to this list as you listen to the Parade that Marches across Your Brain during times of temptation."

I write down several sentences that my Lower Self uses: *I need a filler for my disappointment. I need color and zest to fill my boredom. I don't have*

---

47. This sentence is personal. Maybe you don't have to completely abstain from your bad habit. But then again, maybe you do.

much pleasure in my life, so I need a glass of wine. I need to soothe myself from my mother's critical remarks. I need wine to numb my unhappiness. I have other healthy habits, so this one bad one won't hurt me. I am young and still have time to self-correct when I'm older. I can figure out a way to moderate my intake and not give up wine yet.

He smiles as he sees I have thought about this before.

"Be ready to listen for the same twenty or so rationalizations from your Lower Self," he says. "They will also include these statements: *Just this once. Today is special because it's my birthday, a vacation, the weekend, a holiday. A little won't hurt, and I can get back on the program tomorrow. This anxiety is intolerable because I didn't get what I needed as a child. Don't be so strict. Enjoy life a little. No one appreciates me, so I need to treat and reward myself. A glass of wine will numb my misery about that certain horrible WMD. I can instantly find pleasure and remove the unpleasant feeling I'm currently experiencing.*"[48]

I've heard those exact sentences in my brain when my Lower Self argues with my Higher Self.

He continues. "Here's another popular sentence the Lower Self uses: *You are missing out on a legitimate pleasure. Is this fair?*"

I nod, knowing that ambush sentence well.

"It is a given that your Lower Self will come storming in," he says. "It will always be some form of the sentence, 'Wouldn't it be nice to…' and then it will begin its reasons. As I repeatedly say, you can hear them if you listen to the Parade Marching across Your Brain."

I've never tried this before.

"Your Lower Self will try to persuade you," he says, "that you can indulge *without the price*. It will try to tell you that you are smart enough to figure out how to continue your self-indulgence, and that somehow

---

48. The Lower Self is called the Demanding Child in the book *Skinny School*. In that book, the Higher Self is called Sane Adult, and there is much specific information to help you give up sugar and Trash (junk) Food. There is additional information and help in the free online *Skinny School Advanced* lessons at JulieNGordon.com.

the consequences will not touch or harm you. Your Lower Self does not want to be ruled by your Higher Self."

I've got a rule-breaker streak in me, for sure.

"Step four is to instruct your Higher Self to talk back to your Lower Self in moments of craving, of cues, and of temptation. The key is that you remind your Lower Self that your Higher Self, the judge and jury, has surveyed all the evidence carefully when you were in your best sane mind (not now in the undertow of temptation and craving). The verdict of your Best Sane Higher Self is that you must abstain for your ultimate happiness and well-being."

This is kind of crazy, me talking to me.

He continues. "Say to your Lower Self, 'I hear your ranting and raving, but you do not have my *best* interests at heart. In the morning—my time of peak clarity—my Best Sane Higher Self knows that this bad habit is not right for me.'"

It is true that in times of peak clarity, I know wine is bad for me.

"You've heard all the ambush reasons your Lower Self uses, and you've refuted them. There are no good reasons left, Young Darby. None. So there is really nothing to discuss with your Lower Self."

I guess that's right. I'll have to think about that a little more.

"This battle is fought and won in your mind," he says. "You do not have to give in to a craving. Cravings are urges, not commands, even though their intensity can often feel like a command."

My cravings definitely feel like they are commands I must obey.

"In the morning, your Best Sane Higher Self can find alternate refutations to the Lower Self's prior con job," he says. "Each reason offered up by the Lower Self will be a version of why your bad habit is a legitimate form of pleasure or self-soothing and why you should not miss out. Pay strict attention to your Parade that Marches across Your Brain when you experience a craving."

Listening to the Parade that Marches across My Brain is a new skill, and I still forget to use it.

"Step five is extremely crucial," he says. "Let the craving pass through you as if it is a dart and you are smoke. It is actually good to visualize this during a craving or temptation. You do not have to give in to the urge. Again, it feels like you do, but you don't. Be smoke, and let the dart of the craving pass through you."

I can visualize that, I think.

"Step six is to write down alternate topics you will think about (Rooms to Move Into) or alternate distractions to do when a craving or temptation appears," he says. "Add to this list as you think of other ideas."

Quickly, I write this down: *Look at design magazines. Research recipes online. Take a bath with a good book. Get a cup of herbal tea. Go for a walk with an interesting podcast.*

"This six-part strategy is gold, Young Darby. You can repeat this scenario every time a cue or craving from your Lower Self appears and allow it to pass through without giving in to it."

I can't believe this will work. Nothing else has.

"If your Lower Self is still able to seduce you or ambush you," he says, "this doesn't mean the six-step plan doesn't work. It only means the Lower Self *had a reason that you weren't prepared for.* Listen closely to the reason your Lower Self gives you to indulge. Write that scheme in your Quartz Journal so you can refute it next time. Your Lower Self only has about twenty reasons, not 2,000, why it's okay to indulge this time."

I'm positive I have more than twenty.

"Humans often try to conquer a bad habit and fail," he says. "Then they tend to give up, thinking the goal is too hard."

That's me.

"The road to conquering a bad habit," he says, "is fourfold: try, fail, learn, and repeat. You must write down your Lower Self's schemes because the brain will not recall them when it's under the siege of a craving. Although you have *not* previously listened in to this argument between your brain lobes, now you will, and you will hear the reasons your Lower Self uses to persuade you to indulge, even though you know you are harming yourself."

He wants me to try again. I guess I could.

"Know that if you decide to give in to your Lower Self—your desire for your mood changer of choice, therefore going against your Best Sane Higher Self—you will feel remorseful. The joy of self-mastery will be blocked. The insight as to *why* you desire a mood changer (i.e., the real issue that demands to be medicated) will be blocked as well. You will not move forward emotionally or psychologically."

This is all a little weird, listening in on my self-talk and talking back to myself. But by now, I do understand that I have two brain lobes with different goals, and that creates my cognitive dissonance.

"So at some point, will I be free from craving alcohol?" I ask.

"The grooves will never completely go away," he says. "Even if you've defeated your bad habit for a year or more, suddenly the cravings can reappear. But listen in to the Parade Marching across Your Brain. Your Lower Self will still be using some version of 'Wouldn't it be nice to…' followed by a reason such as, 'I'm sure I can handle alcohol now.'"

"Shouldn't I taper off?" I ask, thinking that I could still drink a little while longer.

"People stop doing bad habits immediately all the time,"[49] he says, "as their brain suddenly realizes that the detriments they are incurring make it ludicrous to continue. They see the battle between their Lower Self and their Higher Self plainly and can now choose. It's almost as if a veil is ripped and the bad habit and its cravings are then viewed with disgust."

I didn't think he'd let me taper off.

"If you can convince your Higher Self that you don't 'want' alcohol (because of the many detriments)," he says, "you can easily and peacefully end the struggle of your brain with this six-step method.

"Genie, I have a lot of childhood issues that still need to be resolved," I say.

"I agree, you do," he says, "but you don't have to deal with your inner childhood demons in order to stop a bad habit. You stop because of the

---

49. If you have a serious addiction, please get some medical help to withdraw.

detriments and benefits and then, only after stopping, will you be *clear* so you can deal with your other issues. Stop first. All you need in order to stop is to plainly, clearly, and loudly (as through a megaphone) *hear the reasons*. Reasons. Reasons. They will bathe your mind and give you the power to quietly choose against your Lower Self that continually pleads for pleasure yet harms you. You wouldn't have a friend around like your Lower Self, always throwing you under the bus for a little fun. Tell your Lower Self that her gig is up."

I know he's right. But I don't know if I can do it.

"The gap between where you are now and your full potential," he says, "will quickly narrow when you conquer your Lower Self and your bad habits."

Since I've tried before and failed, I'm not very confident.

"When you cage the cravings of your lower human heart, a new energy and zest for life will appear. You will again feel optimistic about the future," he says. "You will never create the life you are proud of until you decide you will resist the cries of your Lower Self to numb yourself."

I don't know about a new energy and zest for life. That might be overstated.

"When decades have passed and you have strung together a slew of wasted days and wasted potential because you've indulged in immediate gratification, you will feel the sting of regret and remorse," he says.

"Do you have some alternative ways that I can relax, self-soothe, or entertain myself?" I ask, thinking that my life is pretty stale.

"First, confront the lie that life has few pleasures other than your bad habit. There's the pleasure of reading, the pleasure of seeing, the pleasure of hearing, the joy of learning, the joy of stimulating conversation, the joy of nature, the joy of hobbies, the joy of laughter, and the joy of using your gifts. There is *untold* joy and pleasure to be found without negative detriments attached."

Well, maybe one or two.

"The list is virtually endless but must be made in accordance with your interests," he says. "For some, crossword puzzles or games of solitaire soothe. For others, taking a walk or a bath relaxes them. Yet for others, lunch with a friend, playing sports, gardening, reading, movies, a massage, or hobbies offer comfort and entertainment."

Doing crossword puzzles would bore me out of my mind.

"Another lie to be confronted is that life and fulfillment are found in pleasure, status, power, ease, enjoying your sexual preferences, and the absence of responsibility. The truth is that true satisfaction is tethered to self-discipline, which is required to build a life with contribution (Lesson 5), deep relationships (Lesson 8), and virtue."[50]

"But life is so hard!" I say, thinking how a piddly game of solitaire is not going to solve my despair.

"Yes, life has hardship, loneliness, disappointments, and difficulties," he says. "But your choice to respond to those unwanted scenarios is either self-indulgence or self-discipline. You must quarantine your disappointment while you work to solve your problems. Your Higher Self now knows how to quarantine unpleasantness and how to Move into Another Room in Your Brain. You do not need negative fillers to handle life."

I still think I might.

"Self-discipline is not a harsh taskmaster," he says. "It is a secret sauce that takes you where you want to go. High self-control correlates with productivity, and humans are built to be productive."

And I definitely waste oodles of time.

"Life is lived forward but only understood backward," he says. "So take it from the ancient sages. Overcoming your Lower Self is indisputable for arriving at the end of life and discovering that using your gifts to contribute and having deep relationships are what satisfy."

I don't use my gifts. I have crummy relationships. I have self-indulgence. No wonder I'm a wreck.

"Winning the victory over yourself is the hardest and first battle you must win," he says. "Otherwise, you cannot expect life to turn out the

---

50. The importance that virtue has on happiness is discussed in the free online lessons, *Happy School Advanced*, at JulieNGordon.com.

way you want. Having or not having self-discipline will truly make or break you."

There's so much I need to change.

"Develop a hero's mindset that knows obstacles are inevitable," he continues, "and then rise to meet the challenge instead of slinking into comfort and escape. Be one of the extraordinary. The Lower Self's preference for immediate comfort can only be overruled by a commitment to your Best Sane Higher Self's proclamation."

But can I get through the nightly ambush?

"No scientific discovery will ever eclipse the importance of human beings developing self-discipline," he says. "There is no replacement. Self-control has always been and will always be one of the major secrets to happiness and satisfaction."

I wish there was a pill for self-discipline.

"Of course, it's easier at the moment to lie back and complain about your job, your relationships, politics, your childhood, you-name-it, and then self-medicate instead of taking responsibility for the issues of life, overcoming disadvantages, and making a contribution with your gifts."

Much easier.

"Take full and complete possession of your mind," he says. "Decide how you will behave. Decide what you won't do, what you will do, and then keep the promise to yourself. This is self-discipline, a secret of generations and cultures."

It's so easy to spout off these ideas but way more difficult to implement them.

"When you get your thinking right, it's actually not that hard to avoid the thing that is *harming your life*. In light of that truth, it's not a big deal to quit. The trick to stopping bad habits is to see the reality of the harm. Bad habits are *not* insurmountable impediments," he says in an effort to encourage me.

The Genie swirls into a hurricane funnel of wind and disappears. Speaking of *insurmountable impediments*, my mother is calling. I've ignored her last seven calls, so maybe I should take this one.

"Hi, Mom," I say, feeling my body tense up.

"I've been texting and calling Henry," she bursts out, "and finally today, he told me he doesn't think we're a good match. Things changed after you left my house Friday night and were so rude to Hank. You ruined my relationship with Henry."

This isn't happening. Surely she's not going to blame me for her failed relationship.

"Mom, that's ridiculous that you're blaming me. I didn't want Hank to come over, and when he did, I was appropriately friendly. It's not my fault that you and Henry didn't work out. But I've got to get off the phone because I've got to get to bed. I just tried out a new job tonight, and I'm going to take it. I was a cook! I'm quitting my job tomorrow, and I need to get a good night's sleep."

"What? A cook? A cook? What kind of career is cooking? That's a bad decision, Darby. I can't believe you're quitting your high-paying job to be a cook. You make the worst decisions sometimes. You're single and quitting your job? Darby, I just don't understand you."

I seriously consider hanging up on her. I'm sick of her negativity. Just *sick* of it.

"Mom, you seem to criticize everything I say, so I'm going to get off the phone now," I say. "Maybe we can talk later in the week when you can be more supportive."

"You are so touchy, Darby. You get upset over the least little thing," she says.

"Mom, I told you I was hanging up, so…goodnight," I say and hang up.

She calls back three more times, which, of course, I ignore. Then she starts texting.

"I've never had a child hang up on me in my entire life. It's inexcusable," she texts.

Then she texts, "And by the way, you *are* the reason Henry isn't dating me anymore."

I decide to work on the *stopping bad habits* lesson tomorrow, so I pour myself a glass of wine. Maybe I can come up with a Best Sane Higher Self in the morning. I'm too exhausted to think about it tonight.

Thinking about my emotional disturbance over my mother's call, I wonder What Room I Can Move Into or what other thoughts I can think. A bath with a magazine is always soothing, so I decide to do that. While I'm relaxing in the bathtub, I get a text from Jana.

"I've got clients coming in at 8:00 a.m., and the paperwork is not prepared. I'd like you to be there at 7:00 to help me get ready for the appointment."

Realizing Jana is pulling her stuff again, I chuckle to myself since now I have another job and I'm giving Jana my two-week notice in the morning. Tra-la-la. Finally I can say no to this tyrant.

"Sorry, Jana, but I can't make it in tomorrow until my usual time of 9:00. I'll see you then."

As I click "send," I imagine her blood pressure rising to an unhealthy limit as she reads my text. It is going to be tense in the morning.

Jana texts back, "I am very disappointed in your reply. What could you possibly be doing from 7 a.m. to 9 a.m.?"

I text back, "Sorry. I'll explain in the morning." I won't ever explain it, but after I quit, she'll understand.

Getting ready to fall asleep, I hear my text message ding. It's from my friend Whitney.

Her text says, "My co-worker Nathan who works in IT here at the hospital saw your picture and said you were cute. I told him you were single, and he wants to take you out. Here is his picture."

Another text arrives, and it is a group picture with many people dressed in hospital garb. Then Whitney adds, "Nathan is the one with dark hair on the far left. He is a computer-type and super smart. (You would have genius children.) He also likes music and camping. Can I give him your number?"

Camping? I hate camping. He doesn't sound like my type at all. Not in the least! And in the picture, you can't really see him very well. I type back, "Thanks, Whitney, but it's a little early for me to be dating again." But then I delete that. Thinking of Leland and The Girls, I decide to throw myself back in the fray. So instead, I type, "That's nice of you to think of me. Sure, give him my number."

While waiting for Whitney to text back, I get a text from an unknown number. "Hey, Darby. This is Nathan, Whitney's friend. I'd like to have lunch tomorrow if you're available. Can you meet me at the Moondance Grille at noon?"

Well, at least the guy is not a procrastinator. And what do I have to lose? I would like smart children.

Not wanting to appear too eager, I wait a few minutes and then text back, "Hi, Nathan. Thank you for the invite. Noon would be fine. See you then."

Well, I've got an official date. I probably should have found out more about him before I said yes. But oh well. It's just lunch.

I text my friend who I thought might be interested in subleasing my apartment, and immediately she writes back. She wants to move in ASAP. In fact, she asked if she could move some of her belongings in tomorrow. I will have to hide a key so she can get in. This is all happening so fast. Maybe too fast.

I then text Maggie to let her know I can move in anytime because my friend is going to sublease the apartment. Because Maggie's room is already furnished, I'm going to rent my apartment as furnished and therefore get extra money.

Maggie seems to be happy to have me and writes back, "The green room is waiting for you, so anytime is great. You can start moving your things in tomorrow if you like."

It's too late to pack anything tonight, so I get in bed with one of my favorite magazines, *Elle Decor*. Just for fun, I text Ellie about a magazine spread I see in *Elle Decor* because it was done by a Memphis designer. I know she's up because it's only 10:00 p.m., and she's a night owl. But I wait and wait, and she doesn't text back. I know she sees the text since she keeps her phone with her at all times.

Now I think about texting Nathan back and canceling. Seriously, I have too much going on. But that makes me look bad in front of Whitney. Surely I can spare an hour for lunch. How bad could he be?

Glancing at my mail strewn all over my credenza, I see bills from Anthropology, Zara, Nordstrom, MasterCard, Visa, and American Express. I throw them all in a drawer, thinking I will deal with them soon.

The wine is making me sleepy, so I will think about everything tomorrow. Gosh, I'm a mess. The Genie has never helped anyone as broken as I am. He thinks his little teaching on bad habits is going to help me. I think I'm too much of a loser to be helped. I tell Siri to set an alarm, and I drift off to sleep.

Lesson 5

Discover Your One-of-a-Kind Genius Zone, and Set Your Current Top Life Goals

Monday, August 27

Waking up, I feel unhappy. I know I should start fighting the sadness that is starting to overtake my headspace, but I'm weary.

And I know I said I would try to write out a Best Sane Higher Self proclamation this morning, but somehow, I don't want to. Pouring myself some coffee, I realize I'm *angry* this morning. Why do I feel like that? Emotions come from thoughts, so I back up my thoughts and try to figure it out.

Then I realize why I'm angry. When I woke up, I was thinking about how Ellie didn't text me back last night. I thought about the times when I babysat for her for free, helped her with her two-year-old's birthday party by making her an outrageous princess cake, and took her dinner when she had a baby. When Ellie is around, like at the Vesta Home Show, yes, she's friendly and sweet, but the relationship is not reciprocal. I give way more than she does. The fact that she didn't text me back makes me angry about the way she treats me.

Actually, come to think of it, most of my relationships are disappointing. I don't get the attention and treatment I think one should get in close friendships. Oh, I get plenty of attention from my mother, but it's all negative and critical. I have tried to forge a life of deep, personal relationships with friends, and I have poured myself out for some of them. But they don't reciprocate because I'm not that important to them. Especially after they got married—and doubly when they had babies—did the importance of my existence dwindle.

I think about my last birthday and the sorry way my friends showed up. I'm not asking for hours and hours, but how much trouble is it to buy a birthday card, find a stamp, and mail it? Or would it be unthinkable to spend half an hour of their precious time shopping for me and getting me a small gift?

No, they call when they need something or when it's been so long that they feel obligated to call, talk the minimum time, and then swoosh off to their next more interesting and desirable event. Yep, I'm pretty low on the totem pole for my friends.

I think about a recent text from my sister, Bailey. Her car was in the shop, and she wondered if she could share mine for four days. Hello? Bailey obviously just wanted to save the car rental money. She belongs to the priciest gym in town, drop wads at Zara and Sephora, and makes weekly visits to Stoney River, Season's 52, and Houston's restaurants. But to save a few dollars, it's fine to inconvenience me.

My relationships are some of my biggest disappointments. Honestly, I admit I have resentment toward several people. I don't like the word *hate*, so I will just say I feel an overwhelming dislike toward some people. I'm embarrassed to admit that aloud to anyone, so of course, I don't.

Oh, there I go again. *I just heard my own self-talk, my Parade.* I have sat here for the last ten minutes and thought nothing but negative thoughts. My brain is wired with such deep negative grooves that I can't imagine rewiring my brain like the Genie says. I'm a basket case. Ugh! I've got so far to go before I conquer my negative thinking patterns and the negative emotions and discouragement that follow.

I wish I had told Nathan that I couldn't go on a lunch date today. It's just too much pressure since I'm also quitting my job. I guess that glass of wine I had last night made my brain a little foggy, and I didn't have the clarity to see that today is a bad day to add another stressor. Nevertheless, I pick out one of my cutest outfits, just in case by some miracle Nathan has, well, potential.

On the way to work, I plan what I'm going to cook at Maggie's tonight. I decide to have harissa-spiced pork patties, and I dictate into my phone the menu along with sides. I will run to the grocery store when I get off work and get what I need. Before walking into work, I text Maggie my menu and ingredient list so she can let me know what she already has in stock. She texts back quickly and adds that she loves the menu. It's been awhile since I've received positive feedback from an employer. I like it.

Speaking of employers, the time has arrived to give Jana the news. Although I am happy to quit, I do hate confrontation.

"Jana, do you have a minute?" I ask.

She doesn't look up, letting me know she is perturbed I didn't come in early. "I'm very busy and have been behind all morning. What is it?" she barks.

Walking closer to her desk, I say, "I'm very sorry, Jana, but this is my two weeks' notice."

That got her attention. She instantly stops writing, puts down her pen, and removes her reading glasses. She looks up at me calmly. "What's going on?"

"I found a job better suited for me," I say.

"Alright. Do you want a raise? I'll give you five dollars an hour more," she offers with a softer voice. Jana thinks money solves everything. "And besides, I've got the Taylor divorce proceedings starting this month, so I will need you for at least one more month—or until I can find a replacement."

She's hilarious. I mean, she thinks I care.

"I'm sorry, Jana. Two weeks is all I can do," I reply. I can almost see smoke rising from the dragon's nostrils.

She swivels in her chair, turning her back to me. I breathe a sigh of relief as I head back to my desk. I can't believe I'm finally leaving this dungeon.

I work until 11:45 a.m. and then leave to meet Nathan.

I arrive at the Moondance Grille promptly at noon. My anxiety is pretty high. I have no business being here with all the turmoil I have going on.

The hostess is friendly when I tell her I'm meeting someone. "Are you Darby?" she asks.

Nodding my head yes, she replies, "Your party is already seated," and she leads me to a high wooden booth. My heart is pounding. I hope he's decently attractive.

As I walk to the table, I tell myself to keep my expectations down. Whitney said he was a computer-type.

When I first see Nathan in full view, I realize that not only is he a computer geek, but he's a *squirrely* computer geek. How desperate Whitney must think I am! He has on thick eyeglasses, which he was not wearing in the photo. What's more, he had on a long-sleeved shirt in the photo, disguising the fact that he has absolutely no muscles at all but super skinny arms and legs. Why did I agree to have lunch instead of just coffee? Why did I agree at all until I learned more about him? I am such a nit-wit.

Sitting down, it doesn't get any better. He is not a good conversationalist, and I have to carry the conversation. Looking at my phone, I wonder how many more minutes until I can go. But what is really hurtful is that Whitney thinks I would be interested in a guy like this. I mean, I'm not trying to be mean or snobby—because maybe Nathan is one of those guys with stellar character—but still, what does this say about how Whitney views me? Nathan is in a category of what I would call, well, weird.

Staring into my food, I try to think of another question when I hear a familiar voice. "The food in this restaurant is certainly not as good as my dinner last night." Glancing up, I realize it's Peter.

Oh, no. How I hate that he's seeing me with Nathan. "Hi, Peter. Peter Needleman, this is Nathan McKinley." They shake hands, and I can tell Nathan has a wimpy handshake.

Looking at Nathan, I say, "Peter is the nephew of my new boss, the woman I now cook for." Nathan doesn't know how to make small talk and merely says, "Oh." Peter might sense the discomfort but doesn't show it.

"Nice to meet you, Nathan," Peter says. Turning to me, with one of his confident, expressionless faces, he continues, "I will see you in the kitchen tonight." The horror of Peter seeing me here in a booth with squirrely Nathan is more than I can take. I thank Nathan for lunch and say goodbye, telling him I have to hurry back to work. He doesn't ask if he can see me again, obviously understanding the chemistry was below zero. I hope I wasn't rude to Nathan (I don't think I was), but I'm not in a place where I have energy to be nice to guys on blind dates.

I walk to my car, feeling very alone, hating my life, hating squirrely men, hating bridezillas that marry the Peters. Hating it all. I. Hate. It. All.

Back at the office, I am barely seated at my desk when Jana prances up. "I already found a replacement for you," she says, handing me an envelope. "My younger sister is looking for a job, so she'll fill in until I find the right person. You can leave now. Here's your paycheck through noon today."

This toxic environment could not be good for my emotional or physical health, so I am thrilled to leave. Gathering up my few things, I walk out the door for the last time. I get a bit of an upbeat feeling from my new freedom from Jana.

Walking into my apartment, I see the Genie sitting on top of a box that belongs to my new sublessee who has already started moving in a few of her possessions. All of a sudden, I feel uneasy with everything happening so fast.

I definitely don't have time for another gut-wrenching lesson, so I beg off and ask the Genie for a rain check. After the tension at work, the bummer blind date with Nathan, and the pressure of having to shop for tonight's meal, I cannot handle another lesson. But before I can make my case, the Genie begins.

"Since Jana let you go early today," says the Genie, "as well as the fact that I have already done your grocery shopping for tonight's meal at Maggie's, you now have time for another lesson."

Not having to grocery shop will save me an hour, but my emotions are so tangled that I don't know if I can concentrate.

"Let's add to your arsenal of thinking skills today's important lesson," he says. He has made us both some tea, so I relent and prepare to take notes in my Quartz Journal.

"Since you are now attempting to quarantine your WMDs," he begins, "you will need to replace those thoughts with new, positive thoughts. Today's lesson will provide a valuable Room to consistently Move Into instead of ruminating about your WMDs. Indeed, humans need something of value to occupy their minds."[51]

My problems occupy my mind, that's for sure.

"Today's lesson, *Discovering Your One-of-a-Kind Genius Zone and Setting Your Current Top Life Goals*, is a life-changing exercise," he says, making another exaggerated assertion.

"Genius Zone?" I ask. "What is a Genius Zone?" He has such cockamamie names for things.

"By discovering the three-way intersection of the set of your *skills*, the set of your *interests,* and a worthwhile *need*, you can determine your Genius Zone," he says.

A three-way intersection? What looney thing is he talking about now?

"Before I begin, I want to dispute an unfortunate but prevalent thinking pattern that many individuals possess," he says. "The error is thinking that *a life of ease and constant pleasure* is what makes a human happy. The truth is that theologians and philosophers have known for centuries that a life with deep, true payoffs is *not* one pursuing constant ease and pleasure. Instead, *making a meaningful contribution* with one's skill and interest set is one of the greatest endeavors that will satisfy the

---

51. God is very specific in what we are to think about (see Philippians 4:8).

human soul.[52] Many people waste their life pursuing and indulging in excess pleasure. Only when they reach an older age do they realize how unsatisfying and unfulfilling that pursuit was."

What's wrong with ease and pleasure?

"Not only is it the *duty* of humans to be beneficial to their fellow humans with their skill and interest set, but it is *a secret of their happiness.*"

The ads in my magazines seem to indicate ease and pleasure are a secret of happiness.

"Most people, as you know, have *not* been taught they are the producers and not the victims of their emotions. Therefore, not knowing appropriate strategies to ease or exit their pain, they spend much time and energy merely medicating their pain."

Case in point, my wine.

"But an infinitely better strategy than self-medicating is to discover your skill or interest set and strike out to make a contribution," he says. "Loving excessive ease, entertainment, and idleness is a sure-fire recipe for eventual despair. Leisure is a *reward* for work, not an end in itself. Excessive leisure strips one of self-respect."

I do understand how rotten I feel after a wasted day of movies and wine.[53]

"Dedication to a worthy purpose engages the mind and brings satisfaction," he continues. "It is invigorating to work hard at goals you care about. Having an aim outside of oneself gives the mind purpose, freeing it from the despair of self-absorption," he says.

My only prior aim was to get married. How stupid was that?

"One sign that you are living below your potential is chronic boredom," he says. "You will be unhappy if you are less than you're capable of being. A dull life, one void of color and zest, reveals that a person is living way below their capability. If you play it safe and avoid being all

---

52. Relationships are also a major source of fulfillment (see Lesson 9) as is a relationship with God (see *Happy School Advanced*).
53. Or sugar and Trash Food.

you can be, you are heading toward despair. You must become alive to your potential and discover inspiring work."

The only color and zest I've had in the past were my bad habits.

"Thoughts about using your Genius Zone are actually an amazing antidote to feeling crushed and weighed down," he says. "It is one of the best Rooms for Your Brain to Move Into, away from your WMDs. The world needs your Genius Zone. And it is a healing modality for your chronic boredom, dissatisfaction, and self-loathing."

Chronic boredom, dissatisfaction, and self-loathing—a perfect description of a broken person, aka me.

"People know they are chronically bored," he says, "but fear keeps them in the stands and out of the arena where true living takes place. Humans must throw their hearts over the fence, and their bodies will follow."

"But I don't know exactly what to do," I say.

"That is the purpose of today's lesson," he says. "It is time for you to clarify what you care about and what ignites a spark.[54] Please open your Quartz Journal to List 3, the page titled *Discover Your One-of-a-Kind Genius Zone*. Divide the page into three columns. On the left, list all the *skills* you possess that you can think of. In the center, list all your *interests*."

This won't take long.

"Later, we will come back and address the right column, where you will list ideas on how you might use your Genius Zone to contribute to society."[55]

I'd like to contribute, but I'm always too tired or discouraged.

"Since you need to support yourself, we will discuss today's lesson in terms of discovering the ideal work for you, Young Darby. Even if you were a stay-at-home mother, it is important for you to discover your Genius Zone so you can use and develop it as a volunteer or when you return to the work force."[56]

---

54. Be very prayerful about this decision.
55. Upon finding their Genius Zone, some people prefer to pursue it as a hobby, while others find a way to pursue it as an avenue of work.
56. Many stay-at-home moms can grow in their Genius Zone by using their kids' nap time to study.

Working for Jana was the antithesis of ideal work.

"As you know, if you are not in the right field or job, it is comparable to pushing a cart uphill all day," he says. "Therefore, it is imperative to find work where your gifts and interests are encouraged and work that can support you financially."

This explains why working in a law office and doing administrative work exhausted me.

"After you discover and pinpoint your Genius Zone, immerse yourself in it," he says. "Create a life of being useful with your gifts. Discover where a deep gladness meets a need. There's true joy in offering what you sense you were made to give."

I bet I don't even have a Genius Zone.

"You have a duty to use your skills and interests to repair this world's broken ruins," he says. "Much human flourishing lies on the other side of using talents and interests to achieve worthwhile goals."

"Don't I need to solve my problems before I start exploring my Genius Zone?" I ask, suggesting we should table this lesson.

"I want you to be very proactive in solving your problems," he says. "That's why I gave you three occasions to problem-solve. But you can't swim in your problems all day long or you will drown in discouragement. You must have other topics to think about. Pinpointing your Genius Zone is one of the best Rooms to repeatedly Move Into (to think about) instead of your WMDs."

The Genie signals for me to begin writing. Under *Skills*, I write *Creative. Good learner. Good cook. Good at design. Fairly intelligent.*

(I could have listed a lot more items if he had asked me to list weaknesses.)

Then, under *Interests*, I write *Cooking, all kinds. Design, traditional, modern, and classic. Fitness. Movies. Fashion.* I can't think of anything else.

Although he said we would come back to column three, I ask a question about it. "What do you mean by a contribution to society?"

"What stress, struggle, or suffering can you ease?" he explains. "What needs in the world get your attention? What do you sense you were put on earth to do, to contribute to? What upsets you? What problem do you want to solve? What frustrates you? You provide value by solving people's problems. You live in a broken world, Young Darby, and that creates endless opportunities to repair and redeem. Art, music, and writing redeem; useful products and services repair. There are infinite ways to be helpful or beautiful."

I do care about people's health, and I think cooking is a huge component to helping people with that. And I think lovely living spaces—which is what home design is all about—give people a place to rest and restore. Since my degree is in design, I've always thought I should return to that, but now I'm thinking I love cooking more.

"What you will discover," he says, "is that there are many worthwhile activities from which to choose. But you must learn to say no to some pursuits so you can say yes to your specific goals," he says. "If you don't *narrowly focus* on a few goals,[57] you will be scattered and accomplish little. Therefore, *be exceedingly intentional.* Find your narrow focus, get clear, and get busy. As you progress, you can adjust as needed."

Not only have I not been focused, I've also been on the wrong path.

"You are free to edit, upgrade, or even completely change what you are now writing down," he says. "But for now, the best you can, get started and write out what you think is your Genius Zone."

Reviewing my columns again, I write, "Help people pursue health and enjoyment by creating and cooking delicious and nutrient-dense meals."

"But Genie, I love design, too. Can I do both?" I ask.[58]

"Sometimes people find a way to combine multiple skills and interests," he says. "So for now, go ahead and consider both cooking and design. The path will open to you as you proceed."

I imagine Yoda from *Star Wars*, "Open to you the path will."

---

57. Experts disagree about how many goals one can successfully pursue at one time. The top amount seems to be six, but many think four is the maximum number.

58. For example, Scott Adams, the author of the comic strip *Dilbert*, said he could draw a little, he was funny, and he knew something about business. He combined his skills and interests to create the comic strip.

"Now it's time to write down *specific goals*, your Current Top Life Goals, that is. Turn to this page in your Quartz Journal and decide on four to six Current Top Life Goals."

I write this: *Find my soul mate. Become a great cook or get back into the world of design. Figure out how to give up wine. Get my spending under control.* That's all I can think of for now.

"You don't merely want to be a *goal setter*," he says. "You want to be a *goal achiever*. Therefore, as all life coaches know, you must begin with the end in mind.[59] So write down goals you want to accomplish by ten or twenty years from now. You begin with the end in mind and work backward. Determine the outcome you want, and then make a plan to get there."

Ten or twenty years? I don't even know what I'll be doing by Christmas.

"The secret to *achieving* goals is to formulate a specific plan and then work the plan. A dream is only a dream until you devise a plan," he says.

Now he says I need a plan to achieve my goals, but I'm still not even sure what my goals are. This is all overwhelming.

"Having compelling and exciting goals is imperative to humans," he says. "Humans are aiming creatures, and without goals, humans decay emotionally."

Not having any prior goal except to get married might help explain my emotional disintegration.

"Another important premise to know in this area is that it's satisfying and fulfilling to reach for mastery in an area," he says. "Challenge yourself to reach beyond mediocre within your Genius Zone since there's joy to be found in excellence. Become phenomenally competent in your chosen field. Don't do average work; do killer work."

I couldn't motivate myself to do this for Ogre Jana, but I could easily work for mastery cooking for Maggie.

---

59. Stephen Covey first coined this popular term, but philosophers have known about the concept for centuries. "Where there is no vision, the people perish" (Proverbs 29:18 KJV).

"Modest goals don't inspire humans," he says.

"But large goals frighten me," I say.

"The way to conquer huge goals is exactly the same way one would eat an elephant—one bite at a time," he says. "Daily plow and grind on your goals. Lay bricks every day, and soon you will have built a cathedral. Hudson Taylor described three stages to every project: Impossible. Difficult. Done."

Small, steady steps. I could do that.

"There is too much talk about people being brilliant," he continues. "What is rare and breathtaking is a person who has serious goals and uses discipline to hammer away at them."

"But if I know me, I'll end up procrastinating," I say.

"It is true you will face unwanted tasks when you are trying to reach goals," he says. "Those unpleasant but necessary tasks have been called *frogs*, and you must eat your frogs every day."[60]

Eat frogs?

"Eat them—that is, do the unpleasant tasks early in the day when your Willpower Points are still high," he says. "Your brain will say to you, 'I'd rather not do that unpleasant or difficult task.' But you have to find a way to make yourself eat your frogs every morning. People who are successful make themselves do hard things. Delegate hard things if you can, but there is unwanted responsibility in everyone's life that only *you* can do. Knowing you only have so many Willpower Points[61] available each day is important because you realize that it is best to get high priority items and difficult jobs done early."

"But I'm afraid of failing," I say, thinking about how I now wish I had been more focused in my early twenties.

"Quit playing small and safe, and instead, take calculated risks," he

60. "If it's your job to eat a frog, it's best to do it first thing in the morning. And if it's your job to eat two frogs, it's best to eat the biggest one first." —Mark Twain

61. I can't stress how important it is to be prayerful about setting goals instead of merely *thinking* about what seems good. Carefully, prayerfully, ask God for guidance.

says. "Yes, you will be criticized, and you must brace yourself for that.[62] No one likes criticism, but no one, and I mean no one, ever did anything of substance without being criticized. Don't let the naysayers get you down. They will try, for sure. When the naysayers begin their critical remarks, just remember, you have learned the power to quiet your mind and handle emotional disturbance by Moving into Another Room in Your Brain."

I do like that I am learning how to be in charge of my mind and quarantine negative thoughts.

"Develop some guts, some bravery, and a thick skin (by choosing your thoughts carefully)," he says. "This is the only path to create a life you're proud of. No one is proud of a small, fearful, mediocre life. No one is proud of hunkering down with a mood changer to escape the pressure of doing something important and noble."[63]

Hunkering down with a mood changer was the only answer to trouble I knew.

"As I've said earlier, because of genetics, certain people inherit a more cheery and optimistic thinking style," he says. "Likewise, some people naturally know how to set and achieve goals. But setting and achieving goals is learnable, even if it seems difficult or unnatural."

Why didn't they teach this in school? I could have used this more than plane geometry.

"I am scheduled for a salt bath in Bangladesh, but I will return soon," he promises as he twists into a whirlwind and disappears.

That lesson contained hours—and I mean hours—worth of meat to digest. One thing I now know for sure is that I have not been in touch with my Genius Zone, and by default, I have let the WMDs overwhelm the landscape of my soul. In addition, I have not set goals—much less

---

62. *To Kill a Mockingbird* is arguably one of the world's masterpieces in fiction. But if you look at the reviews, it only gets five stars 80 percent of the time. If masterpieces get criticized, you can expect your work to get criticized.

63. "We are all faced with a series of great opportunities brilliantly disguised as impossible situations." —Chuck Swindoll

tried to *achieve* goals—and that has got to stop. I will have to process all of this information later—as well as the lesson on stopping bad habits—as it is now time to go to Maggie's.

Since Maggie's extra room is furnished, it's just a matter of bringing over my clothes and a few personal items. So I load up my back seat and trunk with my first batch of items, along with the groceries the Genie purchased for me (I guess he purchased them), and head to Maggie's.

As I'm pulling in, I notice Cassie dropping Peter off. He gets out of her car and walks toward his truck like he is going someplace. Even though he's engaged, I admit I was hoping to see him, and I'm disappointed he's leaving. Cassie turns her car around in the large backyard parking area and begins to leave. Hiding behind some large Hollywood sunglasses, she expresses no hint of recognition when we pass. I always feel my spirits drop when women like Cassie snub me. Cassie sees me as a robot who does the blue collar work in life. She sees herself as a ruling blue blood.

Sensing Cassie's absence of interest in me, I feel the downward drag on my emotions, and I know I must fight to get back up to sea level. How exhausting it is to be me, always fighting my negative feelings and thoughts. What should I tell myself? What part of the Genie's teaching do I apply to this situation? I probably need to apply the idea of not *giving negative interpretations to external situations.* Okay, let's see. Maybe Cassie didn't see me. Maybe she is so focused on her wedding that she was deeply in thought. Maybe she has bad eyesight. I almost laugh as I think how I don't believe any of those interpretations. Hey, at least I'm trying! Laughing at myself does actually make me feel a little better.

When Peter sees me, he stops, turns around, and walks toward my car. I can feel my chest tighten.

"Need some help?" he asks with his usual pleasant but stoic face. Where did he get those gorgeous thick eyebrows?

"Weren't you going somewhere?" I ask. "I can carry everything in."

"Yes, I am going somewhere of ultra-importance, and if I help you,

I'm going to be late," he says. "But even more important, I want to know what's for dinner tonight."

He is reliably nice.

He grabs the heavy bags, and I carry the light ones. He doesn't seem in a hurry, so I decide to make a little small talk while we carry in the groceries. "Maggie said you are helping her with a business venture," I say. "What type of business venture?"

"Aunt Maggie and I buy houses that are in disrepair but that are in good areas of town," he says, holding the door open for me. "I renovate them, and we try to get them back on the market quickly and flip them. We are on our third house. We've flipped two of them and have kept one to rent."

"So that's why you and Maggie were at the Vesta Home Show, to get ideas?"

"Exactly," he says, "I need ideas because we are gutting a large old house in midtown that was built in the 1930s."

"I love design and houses," I say. "That was my major in college."

"Did you ever work in design after college?" he asks.

I give him my sad story of getting off the path by selling cheap furniture, blah, blah, carefully leaving out how concentrating on all my failed romantic relationships is really what derailed me.

"Right now, I'm trying to figure out what to do with this huge grand foyer that has a winding staircase," he says. "There's so much wall space, and it all seems rather empty."

I lay the grocery sacks on the counter. Without thinking, I suggest, "Have you seen walls in houses that have not only crown molding but also walls and ceiling patterned with chair molding and trim, creating texture and interest on the wall and ceiling? The design of the woodwork fills up a large empty space and can make a bare wall look spectacular."

Peter doesn't move, apparently trying to visualize that idea. "I've seen molding on walls like that before, but I forgot all about it." He turns to look at me more closely.

Now I'm uncomfortable. I can't think of anything to say, so I just smile. At least my makeup and hair look good since I knew I might run into him.

"Could you go look at the house when you can and give me your ideas?" he asks. "I'm out of ideas overall, and I'd really appreciate it." Peter usually jokes, but right now, I can tell he's serious.

Thinking of how my time has been freed up since I don't have to report to Sergeant Jana anymore, I reply, "I'm moving in here tomorrow morning, but I could take a couple hours in the early afternoon, before I start cooking, to go look at your house. I'll meet you there. What's the address?"

"If you're moving in tomorrow, you'll already be here, so I'll just meet you here at 2:00, and we'll ride together," he says. "I'll have you back by four so you can cook. I don't want you to skimp on the time you spend cooking my dinner."

"Okay," I say, laughing. "Sounds good. Actually, there are few things I'd rather do than look at gorgeous houses." The Genie's talk on Discovering Your One-of-a-Kind Genius Zone comes to mind. I love design as much as I love cooking.

"There are few things I like better than getting free ideas for my houses," he says.

"Don't count on too much help," I say. "I was just lucky suggesting that molding idea."

"Somehow I doubt that," he says. His eyes are warm. Most dark-haired people have brown eyes, but Peter's blue eyes give him a softness. Obviously, Peter thinks I have something to contribute or he wouldn't want my opinion. I hope I don't disappoint him. My mind starts to race at the thought of being alone with Peter tomorrow.

Oh, *stop it*, I say to myself. *Enough of that.* He's engaged, I remind myself. *Quit fantasizing about Peter.* I tell myself that it's unproductive thinking and I am now in charge of what I think.

Maggie walks in the kitchen in her perennially good mood. "Peter, are you pestering my cook?" she asks.

"I'm working quality control, Aunt Maggie. I'm checking the ingredients to be sure they are of the highest quality."

"Well, we're glad you're here, Peter," Maggie says cheerfully. "You can help us carry a load of Darby's belongings up to the green room."

Of course he agrees, and the three of us get everything out of my back seat and trunk and carry it upstairs in one trip.

I briefly saw the green bedroom the other night when it was dark outside. Today, the bright sunlight pours in through the large windows, lighting up a large and most charming room. I walk over to the center window, and there is a perfect view of the neighborhood's majestic houses, their huge oak trees, and Peter's in-law suite. Not that I want to spy on him or anything, but it is an interesting view.

"Is this all you wanted to bring?" Maggie asks, surprised.

Laughing, I say, "No, but I didn't want to scare you."

She laughs, too, and I think how soothing Maggie is to me. Why can't my mother be like that?

"Darby is going to go with me to look at our new house on Peabody tomorrow and help me with some design ideas," Peter says to Maggie.

I'm a little embarrassed that I'm going, even if it is just to help with ideas, since Peter is engaged. I hope Maggie doesn't think I'm forward or that I'm trying to move in on him. "I'm not sure I will be much help, but I'll try," I say.

Maggie smiles as she starts to leave the room. "Darby, you've always been one with terrific ideas. Why, I remember during your college sorority days when you wrote a script for a play that the whole sorority performed. You were never one to be short on ideas."

I had forgotten all about that play and how well it was received. Again, I feel a longing for a mother who would encourage me like this. I hear my self-talk begin to moan a little, but I order myself to *stop it, now*. My mother is the mother I was given, and I must learn to handle my thoughts about her instead of dropping into fantasy thoughts of a nurturing mother like Maggie.

Before Maggie leaves to run an errand, I ask her a question. "Maggie, I don't know how you feel about this, but I like to take early morning bike rides for exercise. How would you feel if I brought my bike? I mean, I don't want to impose on you, but I would need somewhere to keep it."

"Peter rides a bike, too, so maybe he'd let you keep your bike in his spare room where he keeps his," she suggests.

"I wouldn't want to bother him so early in the morning as I often ride early," I say.

"I get up at 6:00," Peter says, "so I can just unlock the door, and you can help yourself to the bike. It's the first room on the left."

I'm definitely uncomfortable with this.

"If you disturb me," he adds, "maybe we can work it out with some kind of additional food, like an omelet one morning." Maggie and I both laugh at Peter trying to get another cooked meal.

He's so nice, as is Maggie. I'm not used to people being this accommodating.

"I'll be right there to put away the groceries," I say. "First I've got to find a recipe in one of my recipe books I brought over yesterday."

The recipe book I'm looking for is in the hall closet, so I accidentally overhear Maggie and Peter talking in the kitchen.

"How did the wedding dance class go?" Maggie asks Peter.

Oh, so that's where Peter and Cassie were this morning, I think to myself.

Peter's voice is not his usual upbeat one. "Instead of a traditional dance, Cassie wants our dance to be some off-the-wall crazy thing. It will take hours to learn those moves, and besides, I don't want to. Why do we have to do some ridiculous dance? Why can't we do the norm, something easy? I'm trying to have a good attitude, but obviously, I don't. I'm not sure what I've gotten myself into."

Maggie is sympathetic. "I can see why you don't want to spend hours learning dance moves. I'm sorry."

Maggie leaves to run errands, and I go back to the kitchen to put away the groceries. When I get to the kitchen, Peter is standing at the fridge. I remind him that there are some leftovers from last night.

Getting filtered water from the spout inside the fridge, he replies, "I'm a little hungry, but I like to have a good appetite when I show up to five-star restaurants." He sits on a bar stool in front of me with his glass of water and a straight face. I lay out my recipes and start washing vegetables.

"How did you like the Moondance Grille?" he asks. I temporarily forgot that he saw me with Nathan earlier today. Embarrassment fills me.

"The restaurant was fine," I reply, trying to decide how to frame the mistake. "A friend set me up on a blind date for lunch," I explain. "It was pretty disastrous. I really need to check things out better before I go on any more blind dates. They have never really worked for me." The whole conversation is still embarrassing. Here I am, ancient, single, and going on unproductive blind dates. I'm such an obvious loser. What a contrast to Peter who's engaged to a gorgeous Barbie doll, ponytail and all.

I must remember that Peter is nice to me because I'm the new cook, and now he might get some new free ideas for his houses. In reality, I'm merely the loser, spinster cook.

"He didn't seem like your type," Peter says.

Before I can respond, Cassie suddenly walks in the back door. "Where's Aunt Maggie?" she demands without acknowledging Peter or me. Instantly I feel caught, being in the kitchen alone with her fiancé. But that is ridiculous, I say to myself. I work here.

He answers, "She just left to run errands. What's up?"

"I forgot to get Maggie's credit card when I was here this morning," she says. "Maggie said she will pay for some of my trousseau, so I need her card to do the shopping." Trousseau is an old-fashioned word, but I do know it means the possessions that a bride assembles for her marriage, such as clothing and linens. Wow! Maggie is off-the-chart generous. My mother has rarely bought me anything of a personal nature unless it was for Christmas or my birthday. I can't imagine being spoiled and pampered by an older woman who treated me generously just to express affection.

"That's very generous of Aunt Maggie," Peter says. "I think she ran to the bank and will be right back." Peter and Cassie seem very businesslike for two people about to get married. Maybe there's still tension between them over their disagreement about the wedding dance.

"I'll text her and see if we can intersect," she says matter-of-factly. She heads back out the door without saying hello to me, without saying goodbye to Peter, and without anything but determination to find a credit card. It's all a little calloused to me. In fact, it seems downright rude.

Peter turns back around and finishes his glass of water without showing any emotion at all. I can't believe Maggie is offering her house for the reception, addressing the invitations, *and* offering to buy Cassie some clothes and linens to help her prepare for the marriage. I guess since Maggie never had kids of her own, this is how she treats her nephew's bride.

"Sorry Cassie is not friendlier," he apologizes. "She's pretty consumed with the wedding."

I want to say *so why are you marrying such a monster?* But of course, I don't. I think Peter is probably going to leave, but he stays on the bar stool.

"I never much liked blind dates myself," he says, continuing our previous conversation, almost as though Cassie hadn't even been here. "Have you ever tried online dating?"

Now I'm about to sink through the floor. Should I lie? "Well," I stutter, "uh, well, yes, a few times, but the dates were disastrous. Some people seem to have luck online, but I never have." I'm sure he can now see that my face has turned bright red with embarrassment. He is quickly discovering what a major loser I am.

"Robby, my best friend and construction supervisor, met his wife online, so I agree that it does work for some people. I tried online dating a few times, too, but it never produced anything lasting for me either."

I'd like to talk about it more, ask him how he met Cassie, and ask all sorts of other assorted questions, but Peter gets up to leave, and I do have to get moving with my meal preparations.

"I'll see you at dinner," he says, and walks out the back door.

When he leaves, I feel that cloud of sadness beginning to descend. The sadness is about my age, Cassie's rudeness, the lack of available Peters in the world, the lack of a nurturing (and sane) mother, and my destiny to be alone and childless. Life seems sad to me. It seems scary, unpredictable, and, in many ways, unfair. But I deserve this. I deserve everything bad because I'm not really a very good person in so many ways. I should be.

I shake my head as I *again* hear my own negative self-talk. What did the Genie tell me to do when I heard myself whining to myself? Oh, Play Hot Potatoes. I'm to kick those thoughts right out of my brain by thinking different thoughts. I command my thoughts to Move into Another Room, which is actually easy since I need to focus on my dinner tonight.

I am only allowed to think about my problems and problem-solve during one of three situations, so I will definitely do that later tonight when I get back to my apartment. Tomorrow I move in here. I hope I haven't made that decision too hastily.

The meal is again met with applause. The guests are telling Maggie that when word gets out about me, she will be booked far in advance. Peter gets a call after dinner at around 7:30 p.m. and leaves. I suspect he's going to meet up with Cassie. I clean up and start back to my apartment around 8:30 p.m. To my surprise, Peter is coming up the driveway when I am pulling out. I can't believe he only sees his fiancée for an hour. He rolls down his window. "Leaving so soon?" he asks.

"Maggie helped me clean up," I say, "and I have to finish packing so I can move in tomorrow."

He slightly nods in an approving manner and says goodnight. I must not let myself think about Peter. He's off the table (like all the good ones).

Ah! Another negative thought! Hot Potato! Hot Potato! What else should I think about? I know, I'll think about some other menu ideas for Maggie's guests.

I've still got a long way to go to retrain my thinking habits, but at least I've started the journey.

While en route to my apartment, Whitney texts me. I read it at a stop sign. "Did you see the posts Bethany put on Facebook?"

I send back a text using my audio: "No, I'm driving, but I will look as soon as I get home."

After pulling into my parking space at the apartment complex, I open up Facebook before I go upstairs. Bethany is on Leland's sofa, taking a selfie of them both. "A good night for a movie" was the post. Ha! She will soon find out that watching movies is all Leland ever wants to do. I'm embarrassed in front of all my friends but actually glad to be out of that boring routine. And I mean boring!

I get another text message. Oh no! It's my mother. "Bailey told me Leland is humiliating you because his new girlfriend is posting pictures of them on Facebook. I'm so embarrassed for you. This is really terrible. I just don't know how you'll ever recover."

I think, *Thanks, Mom. You always know exactly what to say.* I don't text back.

As I walk into my apartment, I consider pouring myself a glass of wine. After all, I haven't had time to completely process the lesson on stopping bad habits. The craving is starting to appear. What am I supposed to say to myself? I was supposed to get clear on my Best Sane Higher Self proclamation, but I haven't done that. I'll have to work on it tomorrow, I think as I pour myself a big glass of Chardonnay.

Life is a huge disappointment. I hate this unhappy feeling. I hate it. All I want to do is go to sleep and forget my horrible, lonely life.

Lesson 6

Rooms to Stay Out Of:
Self-Pity, Failure, and Regret

Tuesday, August 28

Before I even get out of bed, I am again plagued with the thought that I'm going to be single and childless the rest of my life. Although I had hoped for a life filled with intimacy and closeness, I am now resigned— stop, I say to myself. STOP! I hear the Parade. The incessant, march of a Parade that peeks around every corner in my mind.

I must, I must, I must remember I'm not the *victim* of my emotions but the *producer* of them. And by changing my daily thoughts, I can change my emotions. Apparently, changing my thoughts is a new skill to learn, comparable to memorizing the dictionary.

After getting some coffee, I realize I need to process the two previous lessons, the one on stopping bad habits as well as the one on discovering my Genius Zone. I guess I'll start with the lesson on stopping bad habits.

Opening my Quartz Journal, I again read through the six steps to stopping bad habits. I add more ideas to each of the six steps. This morn- ing, I truly do feel sane. I do see—after reviewing these lists and my notes from the Genie—that my Best Sane Higher Self wants zero alcohol. I see how I have competing brain lobes and how my Lower Self pulls a con job. I look at what I wrote down for my Best Sane Higher Self and know that tonight, when the craving comes, I am going to fight back. Yes, I am going to talk back to my Lower Stupid Self. Although the wine dials down my sadness and loneliness at the moment, it's a con job because it leaves discouragement, decreased health, and less motivation in its wake. Yes, tonight the battle will begin.

Moving on, I try to process the Genius Zone lesson. Again, I review my notes from the Genie's rampage. I love cooking, but I also love design. I'm not sure what to do. At least I know that one of those areas is where I should look for permanent work (instead of my wasted years selling cheap furniture, arranging flowers, or, worst of all, doing administrative legal work.)

Thinking about the choice of cooking or design puts me in a better frame of mind. The Genie was right that I need a Room to Move Into, something to think about that is positive, instead of always brooding over my WMDs.

Looking at the clock, I decide I should probably work on my Current Top Life Goals at another time. So I scribble down a few more thoughts and then start packing clothes to take to Maggie's.

Around noon, after loading everything I can into my trunk and back seat, I put my bike on the back of my Lexus. On the way to Maggie's, my mother calls, and I decide to take it. First, I brace myself emotionally and warn myself to make the conversation short.

"Hello, Mom," I say pleasantly, hiding my disappointment that she called.

"Do you still remember me? I'm the woman who birthed you. I thought maybe you had forgotten me since you never call," she says, always finding something to scold me about.

"Mom, I talked to you two days ago. I'm thirty-two, and I'm not going to call you every day anymore. Anyhow, I'm very busy today," I explain. "I am moving to a different location in connection with my new job, so I'm pressed for time."

"Moving? You're moving, and you haven't told your mother? When did all this happen? And how could you be so busy since you're not dating anyone?"

It's downright emotionally abusive for her to talk to me like that. "Mom, I'm in a hurry. Sorry. What did you want?" I feel all my prior agitated feelings that I associate with her resurfacing.

My mom continues without skipping a beat. "Bailey has agreed to give me $300 a month out of her inheritance from your father since that money she got from him should really be mine. I want you to give me some monthly money, too. After all, if it hadn't been for you, I probably would've married Henry."

My blood starts to boil. "I'm sorry, but Daddy left that money to me," I say. "If you get old and can't pay your bills, then of course I will help you." I am burning with intense anger at her that she's blaming me again for losing Henry.

She raises her voice and starts her usual arguing. I interrupt. "Mom, I've got to go. I'm very busy. I'll call you another time."

"Sure," she says, "like in a month?"

"Mom, I've got to go. I'm going to hang up."

"You're not going to hang up on me *again*, are you?" she shrieks.

"Like I said, I'm very busy right now. I'll call you back soon. Sorry, I've got to go. I'm hanging up now. Goodbye," I say as I tap the red button on my iPhone to end the call.

As I'm driving, I can feel myself begin to shake. My mother is truly deranged. Sick. Mentally unfit. It's almost as if she is two different people, one to Bailey and the other to me. Bailey has somehow been protected from her madness, while she has always expected me to be both her confidant and her loyal servant.

I can't believe Bailey is giving her $300 a month. Although my mother has plenty of money for food, rent, and necessities, she doesn't have the discretionary money she'd like. Despair over my emotionally challenged mother approaches.

Hot Potatoes! Hot Potatoes! Think about something else, I command myself. *Do not think any more thoughts about your disturbed mother right now.* I decide to think about something neutral such as how to organize the belongings I've just brought to Maggie's. Where will I put everything?

Pulling into Maggie's driveway, I notice that no one else is around. It takes me three trips to carry everything up to my room, except, of course, my bike. I am grateful for the extra closet down the hall that Maggie made available for all my many clothes. Looking out the big window in the green room, I see Peter pulling up in his truck. He is wearing gym shorts and a T-shirt and carrying a child-sized baseball bat. I wonder where he's been this early in the day with that sporting equipment. His slim build reminds me of a college athlete.

Peter and I are scheduled to leave at 2:00 this afternoon to walk through his house. I brought my groceries for tonight with me, so at least that's done. It's almost 2:00, so I freshen up and walk downstairs.

Peter has changed clothes and is back in his usual jeans and work shirt. "Let's put your bike in my spare room, and then we can go," he says. Together we walk into his apartment, and he puts my bike in an empty room. While he's gone, I look around quickly and find there aren't many pictures on the wall, and the furniture looks rather tired. I suppose Cassie is fixing up a cozy place for them to move into.

Ten minutes later, we are inside his Ford F-150 driving toward his new acquisition. I can't help but think he is the most attractive guy I've ever met. I mean, what's not perfect about him? Even his truck, although several years old, is immaculate, unlike my Lexus that still has the last two weeks' Starbucks coffee cups on the floor.

I get ready to ask about the house we're headed to, but before I can, he starts the conversation. "What have you been doing all day?"

A little startled by how personal that is, I fish around in my head for what to say. I certainly don't want to tell him I had to recover from a painful conversation with my demented mother. I can't think of anything worthwhile to say, so I start talking about my early morning bike ride.

"Did you know this part of town has bike paths everywhere?" he asks. "The Memphis Greenline bike and hiking path is just a couple blocks away."

"I love the Greenline," I say. "I've seen lots of bikers on it when my friend Whitney and I have walked on the east end of it. I'd like to know where the west routes are." Noticing Peter's hands on the steering wheel, I see how strong and beautiful they look. I'm pathetic, thinking about a guy's hands.

"I'll show them to you," he says.

I want to ask him where he was this morning with that youth-sized baseball bat, but maybe later because we are now arriving at his newly acquired mansion. As I survey the house's exterior, I almost feel a pang of sorrow because it reminds me of a grand old dame, amazing in her prime but now in a state of major deterioration. "Oh my!" is all I can say.

"Lots of possibilities, wouldn't you say?" Peter asks as he gazes admiringly at his purchase.

"Old houses have a definite charm," I say, still stunned at the degree to which this house's elegance has been lost.

Suddenly, I feel Peter looking at me. I turn to look at him, and our eyes meet. We do have a connection. For him, it must be because we both admire this old house. For me, it's a sadness that when I finally meet someone who is ideal, he is taken. The eye contact is a little too long, and I feel uncomfortable, so I open my door and hop out.

The interior of the house has suffered similar neglect. Although the rooms have extremely high ceilings, they are otherwise small and dark. The wood floors look beaten, and some rooms have four different designs of wallpaper rolling off the walls.

My mind is bursting with ideas, but I decide to let Peter speak first. "Well, what do you think?" I ask, thinking he will talk about moving walls, opening up space, and adding lighting.

"I wonder who lived here," he says soberly. "I wonder what their struggles were. Did they love each other? Did they quarrel over children or finances? Were they happy here?"

My heart aches as he says this. Peter is obviously someone who gets the deep issues of life. How I would love to live in a house such as this and be the next story inside these walls with a wonderful husband and a baby. There I go again, focusing on a WMD. I shake it off pretty fast, though, as I have mental work to do.

"I'd love to hear the secrets in these walls, too," I say. Peter turns and looks at me again. There is no smile, but his penetrating eyes communicate a connection again.

"Are you ready to hear my ideas?" I say, quickly changing the subject and breaking eye contact.

"Already? You already have ideas?" he asks.

Then I begin to unload.

"What if you tore out this wall? And then what if you moved the dining room from here to over there? What if we opened up this space for a state-of-the art kitchen with a huge keeping room?" On and on I go. "Then over here we could tear down this wall and install a huge bay window."

"Darby, you amaze me," he says, looking at me again with one of those piercing stares. "Why are you not an architect or an interior designer?"

Again, I don't tell him the truth—that I've wasted ten years trying to get married to the wrong men.

"Let me call Robby, my construction superintendent," he says, "and see if he's free to come over. I want him to hear you explain these ideas and see if they are feasible." Robby, I remember, is the friend who found his wife online.

Robby is free, and in fifteen minutes, he arrives with his tape measure and notepad. For the next ninety minutes, the three of us brainstorm what we could do to the house. When we are ready to leave, Robby asks me, "Are you a designer or an architect?"

Peter turns to me. "Darby, that's the second time that question has been posed to you today."

Stumbling around and rather embarrassed, I say, "Well, I, actually… I'm a cook," I say.

"A cook?" Robby asks.

"Uh, yes, currently," I say. "I do have a degree in design, and I've been reading design magazines for fifteen years, but I'm not a professional."

"Could have fooled me," Robby says in his friendly, Southern drawl.

"Don't give her any ideas," Peter says. "She's now cooking for Aunt Maggie's bed-and-breakfast guests, and I'm enjoying it, too, so don't rock the boat, man."

Robby laughs. He is used to Peter.

On the way back to Maggie's, Peter and I are silent for the first couple of minutes.

"Tired?" he asks.

"Heaven's no," I say. "That was ridiculously fun. I feel energized from our time at your house."

"You are quite the machine, Darby. It's fun to watch you in action," he says, glancing at me while he drives.

I look back at him. I don't know how to respond to that compliment, so of course, as usual, I say something stupid. "Your house is going to be amazing when it's finished. I can already see it in my mind."

"You can?" he asks. "So in your mind, who lives there?"

"I haven't thought about the people yet," I say, lying. I have definitely thought about living there with Peter, but as soon as that fantasy presses in, I Hot Potato it right out.

"What kind of house do you want someday?" he asks.

There he goes again, being so nice, asking questions about me. "That is exactly the type of house I want someday. Something grand and majestic with character. I love your house."

"I thought maybe you would," he says. I look at him, and he is already looking at me with a very serious face. My stomach turns upside down, feeling the chemistry, but then I remember that he's engaged and only wants my free ideas.

When we get back to Maggie's, it's 4:15 p.m., fifteen minutes late to begin my work for tonight. Maggie is in the kitchen when we arrive. I'm getting ready for a whipping since I'm tardy, something like Jana always gave me whenever I was late

"I'm sorry I'm late," I say.

"Darby, in the last three days, I haven't been this relaxed since I opened this bed-and-breakfast. I certainly can't get upset over fifteen minutes. You know what you're doing. I have full trust in you."

I almost want to cry. After Jana treated me like a robot for two years and with my mother constantly criticizing me for thirty-two years, I can't believe someone actually believes in me and gives me the benefit of the doubt.

Going into one of my Genius Zones, I focus like I'm cooking for the POTUS.

With all my added effort, everything is actually ready early, so I put it all in the warmer and wait for Maggie's guests to come down. With my extra time, I clean up the kitchen.

Maggie notices the clean kitchen when she enters. "My, you're so organized."

"Not really," I say, laughing a little. "I just read over my recipes for tomorrow, and I realize that I forgot two ingredients at the grocery store. I think I'll make a quick run there tonight after I do the dishes."

"Why don't you go while we're eating?" she asks. "You've already got the kitchen cleaned up. That way you can be back before dark."

"Thank you," I say. "It won't take long, and I'll be right back to finish the dishes."

"Do you mind getting some coffee while you're out?" Maggie asks. Like me, Maggie likes to grind her fresh coffee beans every morning.

"Of course," I cheerfully say. In my opinion, coffee's importance in the morning is right up there with oxygen.

Arriving at the grocery store, I pick out some garlic and parsley and then head to the coffee aisle. There, to my surprise, standing in the aisle surveying the coffee, is Leland! He must have just gotten off work because he still has on his long, white physician's coat. We are both shocked to see each other.

"Darby!" he says with an affectionate tone and look.

"Hey, Leland," I say with an edge. He has humiliated me, and I have not forgotten. Leland never grocery shopped while we were dating. I used to do it all. I guess he hasn't trained his new dog to do that trick yet.

"I've been thinking about you," he says quietly and sincerely.

I'm caught between being disarmed by his softness and being angry at how he used me for so long. Before I can respond, Bethany walks up from the other direction, obviously not seeing me.

"I found some meals we could microwave," she says to Leland. "Would you rather have Stouffer's lasagna or Stouffer's alfredo pasta?"

I can't resist what I say next. "Stouffer's lasagna is always a good choice." My words are not lost on Leland, and he grins. He always said I made the best lasagna in the world and how happy he was to no longer have to eat Stouffer's.

Realizing it's me, Bethany mutters, "Oh. Hi, Darby."

"Have a good dinner," I say and walk away. I knew Leland would eventually quit taking The Girls to expensive restaurants since his farm boy frugality is embedded deeply into his neural grooves. But I must admit, I am getting some satisfaction seeing him return to Stouffer's.

Driving back to Maggie's, I remember Leland saying he had been thinking about me. He definitely had a look of honesty on his face when he said it.

I enter the back door to Maggie's kitchen, and Peter meets me there with an armload of dishes. "You're three for three," he says, meaning that tonight's meal was another success.

I wonder why Peter eats dinner with Maggie and Cassie isn't invited. I overheard Maggie and Peter talking about Cassie leaving soon for her weekend bachelorette party. I think maybe they said it was this weekend.

Peter runs hot water over a few plates and stacks them on the counter. He opens the fridge and asks if there are any more peanut butter cookies.

"Look in the freezer," I say. "There are several more."

"Don't count on there being any more in the morning," he says. "I like to get a midnight snack."

Surprised, I ask, "You mean you walk over here, disarm the alarm, eat, and reset the alarm?"

"When I'm hungry," he says, "which is every night at 1:00 a.m." He sits on the bar stool and eats his cookies while I finish loading the dishwasher.

Even though it's none of my business, I am curious about Cassie. Why is she never around? I decide the timing is still not right to ask.

Maggie is performing her evening chores such as blowing out candles and turning on dimmers before she comes in to help me with the last dishes.

"How are you doing with addressing the invitations for Cassie?" I ask Maggie.

She rolls her eyes, and I detect her annoyance. "Cassie wants them to go out this Friday, and I still have 200 to address."

"Maggie, I can finish the kitchen by myself," I say. "Why don't you go work on the invitations?"

She gazes gratefully at me. "Why, thank you, Darby. That is very considerate. This is exactly how I remember you from twelve years ago."

Peter is looking at me, too, with his usual expressionless face. "I *guess* I could help Darby, Aunt Maggie," he says with feigned reluctance.

"Thank you, Peter," says Maggie, smiling and grabbing the box of invitations.

Before Maggie exits, I ask, "Do you want me to get up and help you serve your guests breakfast?"

"Darby, I don't pay you for that, so no. Besides, I enjoy fixing breakfast for everyone. You are doing the lion's share by providing dinner. That is very sweet of you, though."

When she leaves, Peter walks over to the sink. "The dishwasher is full," he says. "Do you want me to wash or dry the rest of the dishes?"

"If I get to pick," I say, "you wash, I'll dry." He nods and begins. We don't talk for a minute or so. I eye him carefully from the back as he stands at the sink with perfect posture and with his weight equally distributed between both feet.

I break the silence. "By the way, thank you for letting me keep my bike in your spare room. I was thinking about a bike ride in the morning, but I don't want to disturb you when I get it."

"As I said, I get up at 6:00," he says. "Are you going before that?"

"Not hardly," I say and laugh. "I had planned to go around 7:00. Should I just knock on your door to get my bike?"

"I'll unlock the door, and you can help yourself," he says.

"I'll try to be quiet," I say. I want to ask Peter about the child's baseball bat, but a male guest enters the kitchen and engages Peter in a discussion about buying real estate. I can read between the lines, though, and Peter is not very excited about talking to this guy. Soon after the dishes are done, Peter excuses himself from the guest and retires to his in-law suite. The guest's incessant talking wore me out, too.

After everything is finished in the kitchen, I go upstairs to my room. This is my first night at Maggie's. It's still early, so I decide to organize some of my things.

Surprisingly, the Genie arrives. "Genie," I say, "won't everyone hear you?" It's my first night at Maggie's and I want to settle in, not get another heavy lesson.

"No one can hear me but you," he says, "so let's get started." He sits on the floor in the traditional cross-legged lotus position.

"In our next three lessons, Lessons 6 through 8, I am going to teach you about some Rooms in Your Brain to Stay *Out Of*. Unhappy people always have negative emotions, and you now know that emotions are produced from thoughts. You also know that you can listen in to the Parade that Marches across Your Brain (listen in on your own thinking) and consciously choose to Change Rooms (think about something else). In these next three lessons, I want to highlight some quicksand areas that many humans in every generation fall prey to."

I'm probably guilty in all three areas.

"In tonight's lesson, Lesson 6, I will teach you how to think about self-pity, past failure, and subsequent regret. In Lesson 7, I will teach you other Rooms to Stay Out Of such as being offended, being angry, and being resentful. And Lesson 8 will give instruction on still other negative Rooms to stay out of, the Rooms of worry, anxiety, and fear. Learning how to think correctly about these subjects will skyrocket your personal peace and happiness because, as you now know, your thoughts produce your emotions."

Those topics are 90 percent of my current thoughts.

"Let's get started with some Rooms that you frequently visit," he says, "the Rooms of self-pity, past failure, and subsequent regret. These Rooms are devastating to your happiness."

I may have some issues with thoughts about failure and regret, but I don't have self-pity.

"Self-pity is feeling sorry for yourself," he begins, "because you don't have more of something. Self-pity can be from not having certain physical attributes or from not having certain talents or gifts. Self-pity can come from thinking one has not had the same opportunities or advantages that others have had, or from feeling violated or harmed by others."

Maybe I might have a *tad* of self-pity.

"Self-pity can come from feeling trapped in a situation," he continues, "or from not having something specific one truly desires. Maybe a person doesn't feel they have received enough attention or appreciation from others. The sources of self-pity are infinite, but in every case, self-pity means one feels sorry for themselves because they don't have enough of something."

Like no boyfriend.

"I admit hard things happen," he says. "People are left in relationships, and they are fired, maimed, and forgotten. Accidents happen, people fail in careers, they endure theft, or they have health issues. Horrendous events like war, pandemics, and murder occur."

Those are all terrible.

"What is striking, though, is that individuals *with the exact same situations or circumstances* often give their circumstances completely different interpretations (remember Lesson 3?). For example, one person feels victimized by fate and carries a sense of being injured (thus feeling sorry for themselves), while another person—remember, one with the exact same circumstance—does not feel sorry for themselves."

I don't understand this.

"The difference, as we learned in Lesson 3, is in the value and interpretation that humans assign to all situations and circumstances," he says. "When hard things happen, the responses of people usually fall into two general camps. One group will initially spend a few moments feeling sorry for themselves but then quickly Move into Another Room in Their Brain and think about something else (or problem-solve if it is one of the three specified times). In the second camp, people continue to negatively ruminate about their situation and decide they are victims, blaming others, feeling sorry for themselves, and developing self-pity."

I'd better set him straight on this. Although I realize I do have some self-pity, I have an excuse.

"Genie, I had a very difficult childhood and didn't get what I needed to emotionally mature properly," I explain. He needs to understand that my issues are not my fault.

"Young Darby, you did (and still do) have a difficult family-of-origin, but you are an adult now. You must take responsibility for your life and never blame anyone again. Self-pity and blaming are tools immature people use so they don't have to take full responsibility for their lives. Refuse to indulge in this."

Well, I, uh, do blame my family-of-origin for my current issues. He's telling me to quit that.[64] How would that be possible? I've been blaming them for years.

"Whatever your circumstances, you can develop an increased ability to regulate your thoughts and thus your emotions, Young Darby. Having a victim mentality and thus self-pity is one of the *greatest weaknesses of the human spirit*."

---

64. If you are a Christian, you have all the resources in Christ that you need. God's grace is sufficient for all your needs.

This couldn't be right.

"Self-pity is an acid to the human soul," he says. "Of course, you didn't script certain situations on purpose, but they are here. Now the question is this: *What interpretation are you going to give to them?*"

How about *I was unfortunate when they gave out mothers.*

"You do have a choice," he says. "You can feel sorry for yourself and whine and complain about how hard and unfair your circumstances are. Or you can choose to be one of the rare, the magnificent, and the noble who takes charge of their thoughts and refuses to have self-pity. These people take their unwanted situations and apply a better interpretation to them."

Rare? Magnificent? Noble? That's certainly not me.

"They insist in their minds that other people's inconsideration and harm (and other difficult situations) will be a springboard from which they will find a silver lining," he continues. "Those people are the emotionally healthy in life, believing there is *opportunity in obstacles.* Noble people have powerful and inspiring goals and press toward them *in spite of* obstacles and difficulties."

I thought those people only existed in works of fiction.

"Perhaps in your opinion, you've been dealt some difficult cards," he says, "but replaying in your mind how difficult your circumstances are is a complete, monumental waste of energy and time."

I do spend a *lot* of time thinking about my dreadful circumstances.

"What I am saying to you over and over again in *Happy School* is that you get to choose the mental landscape you are going to live in by constantly monitoring the Parade that Marches across Your Brain, interrupting your self-talk, quarantining your negative thoughts, refuting the negativity by telling yourself another story, and then by choosing more profitable thoughts (Moving into Different Rooms). You are in charge of your thoughts, and that includes being in charge of giving an interpretation to everything that happens to you."

He keeps coming back to the fact that I am responsible for my thinking.

"There is no time for self-pity if you are focused on achieving mastery in your Genius Zone and on giving away your skill and talent set," he says.

I still need to process the lesson on my Current Top Life Goals.

"Humans express self-pity so others will feel sympathy for them," he says. "But in contrast, self-pity actually causes others to lose respect for them."

I thought I was just sharing my problems. I didn't know it was a plea for sympathy.

"Currently, you've got a neural groove in your brain—remember the schoolyard path metaphor?—that you are someone who has been treated unfairly by life, by other people, and by fate. It's horrendously destructive, Young Darby. You must replace the self-pity neural groove you've dug into your brain. It will take some work, but remember, *Happy School* is a five-year program. You will not even recognize yourself if you work diligently on what I teach you in these lessons."

I'll be thirty-seven in five years, practically in the grave.

"Now I want to discuss your thoughts about your past failures, Young Darby, and the subsequent regrets you have."

"My past is replete with failure and regret. It haunts me," I admit.

"Humans' pasts often have many mistakes, foolish behaviors, and other self-defeating behaviors. You must forgive yourself for your past shortcomings. Will yourself to see your past failures *as an opportunity for growth*. Realize that great suffering often leads to great positive change."

Oh no. More hooey that suffering leads to positive outcomes. I don't know if I can take it.

"People allow themselves to watch their past Failure Movies in their mind," he says, "movies of situations that did not go the way they believe they should have. You must never indulge in this. Instead, grab your thoughts like a cowboy would grab a calf in a rodeo ring, and wrestle it to the ground. Reason aggressively with your voice of inadequacy, and turn off your inner critic. It is a total waste of time to wish for a different set of circumstances or play a Failure Movie in your mind from the past, hoping somehow for a different outcome."

I do this all the time.

"It is a similar waste of time," he says, "to replay the movie wondering, 'If *only* I had instead done this or that.' The past is over, so thinking about it—except to learn from it—is unproductive."

Again, the if-only-I-had-acted-differently movies are ones I play frequently.

"Instead, see your failures in a new light," he continues. "If you read or listen to biographies of great men and women, they invariably point to their failures as the springboard to their success. This is about your mind, Young Darby. This is about guarding your mind's thoughts, insisting that you use your past failure merely as feedback."

My failures may be one of my favorite topics.

"Yes, of course you have past failure, but learn from it, gather your strength, and strike out again. Refuse to let the failure define you," he says. "Some person is rising from abysmal failure every minute."

I doubt I will.

"Draw a line in the sand, and tell yourself that after you have dissected your failure for possible wisdom or learning, you will then quarantine the event, guarding your mind from your negative self-critic. Again, this is about learning to listen to your Parade and then Moving into Another Room."

Here it comes again: take control of my thoughts.

"Think of your brain as the owner of a large apartment complex," he says. "You decide what tenants are allowed to live there. Do you allow the tenant (thoughts of self-pity, failure, and regret) to destroy your property? Or do you screen to find desirable tenants to live in your mind? You choose the thoughts that get residence. You are the owner of your mind."

More harassment about taking responsibility for my thoughts.

"Your brain has an amazing power," he says, "because you can choose your thoughts. The neural grooves are deep but can be rewired. I will return soon, Young Darby, and we will discuss another Room for you to Stay Out Of," and in an instant, he spins into the air and is gone.

Sitting in Maggie's lovely green room, I realize I am *full* of self-pity. I mean, I feel terribly sorry for myself. My critical mother, my non-reciprocating sister, my self-centered ex-boyfriend, my childlessness, my unconcerned friends, the list goes on and on. I feel sorry for myself all the time. And I had no idea! I have been completely blind to my own self-pity.

And how much time do I waste playing old Failure Movies? I'm momentarily stunned at the depths to which I've allowed my mind to sink.

A glass of wine right now would sure drown out how badly I feel about my self-pity. Before the craving can fully bloom, though, I chop off its head, telling myself, *When I'm in my Best Sane Higher Self, I know that I don't want myself to ingest poison, and I'll be glad in the morning that I resisted, even if my Lower Self is pleading now.* Wow! I caught the ambush early and used my Best Sane Higher Self proclamation to tell my Lower Self no.

Fast! Hurry! I tell myself. Move into Another Room. What do I think about? Earlier I was going to organize some of my belongings, so I will briefly do that before I get ready for bed.

I made it one night without wine. Good for me.

Wednesday, August 29, 6:15 a.m.

The sunlight streams through the window as I turn off my alarm before it goes off. Actually, that was the best night's sleep I've had in a while. I know alcohol disrupts one's sleep cycle. My Best Sane Higher Self is glad I abstained.

Although I am glad I didn't drink last night, I try to Move into Another Room, but I can't think of anything to think about. Opening my Quartz Journal for ideas, I decide to command my mind to review my Genius Zone lesson from yesterday. Soon I realize how much I enjoy thinking about design as well as cooking, so I first Move into the Room of designing Peter's house. Then I Move into the Room of cooking for Maggie's guests. Listening to the Parade and then knowing how to Move into Another Room is one of the world's best secrets for emotional health. Knowing I have the ability to think another thought is, as MasterCard says, priceless.

Usually I don't put on any makeup to ride my bike, but today I put some on—just in case I run into Peter. Also, I make sure I wear a cute workout outfit—again, just in case.

Grabbing my bike helmet and walking toward his suite, I notice the coolness of the morning before the Memphis sun starts its normal end-of-August oppression. Having had a better morning than usual, I can detect a sense of pleasure from being outside in the early morning. As I walk up to Peter's door, he opens it before I can knock.

"I've got a twenty-five minute ride all laid out for us," he says. "That is, if you don't mind if I come." He's dressed in work-out shorts and a T-shirt with his helmet in his hand.

He's going to ride with me? I'm stunned, and I know Cassie would hate this. Where is that girl? She's rarely around. I've never seen engaged people spend so little time together.

"So you're going to be my tour guide?" I say, feeling stupid that I can never think of anything witty.

"If that's okay," he says, looking at me like a fifth grader asking permission to sharpen his pencil.

"I'd appreciate learning the routes around here," I say.

We hop on our respective bikes. Peter's bike is an older model, and mine is a new cruiser. Sadly, I realize that my love of new things has gotten me in trouble, but I quickly dismiss that downer thought as we head across the street to the bike path.

"Hope I can keep up," he says with a straight face.

Since I ride a lot, I feel pretty confident that I won't embarrass myself.[65]

---

65. In the book *Skinny School,* one learns how to correctly think about exercise.

We're off. Down Madison Avenue, over to the Green Line, and back again. Twenty-five minutes into the ride, Peter pulls into a small, renovated building that houses a Starbucks. I'm sweating profusely, breathing hard, and gulping water. He barely looks winded.

"You're in good shape," he says. "That was a good workout. Do you have time to stop for coffee and talk about my house?"

Now I'm very thankful I took time to put on some eye makeup and lipstick. Again, I think of Cassie and feel guilty for having coffee with her fiancé. But hey, I'm just helping with design ideas, right?

"Yes," I say, "but I don't have any money for coffee."

"I think I can cover it today," he says. We lock up our bikes, grab a couple coffees, and come back outside to sit at a table with an umbrella. The endorphins from the bike ride, the beauty of the early morning, and the thrill of being with Peter all collide to make me feel pretty decent, quite an upgrade from my usual Debbie Downer morning mood. This sure beats the heck out of getting ready to go to work for the warden.

Sitting at the table, we review some of the revisions he is going to make to his house on Peabody Street. "Darby, I'd like to officially hire you. There's a lot of work to do, and I not only need help with design, but I also need help picking out appliances, floors, light fixtures, wrought iron, and paint colors."

"I'd love to help you," I say, "but I only know what I like, and I don't have professional experience." At that moment, a memory appears of an interior design professor I had in college who told me I had impeccable taste and scale. Why, oh why, have I wasted the last ten years?

"My hunch is that you know exactly what you're doing," he says. "It's okay if you make a mistake or two. I paid my last architect-designer thousands of dollars, and I'm sure you'll be much less expensive than she was. Anyhow, I'm thinking of keeping this house and moving into it."

Oh, so this is where he and Bridezilla will live. Well, I don't want to be involved with her. How do I beg out of this?

"Thanks, but I don't think so," I say.

"Why not?" he asks. "I thought you needed some more work."

What do I say? How do I get out of this?

"Well, I, uh...." I can't think of an excuse.

"Are you afraid you won't do a good job?" he asks.

"No, I think I can do it," I answer, as I remember how I have played around with kitchens using my CAD software.

"Did you already find some other work?" he asks.

"No, I haven't," I say, racking my brain, frantically trying not to tell him that I don't want to work for Bridezilla.

"Well, I guess I don't understand," he says. "You'd just rather not?" he asks.

"Actually, I know I would enjoy it, but..."

He waits for more, but I can't think of what to say. Finally I say, "I don't think I can have it done in six weeks."

"Six weeks? You don't have to have it done in six weeks. We'll do it as quickly as we can, but there's no pressure," he answers.

Hmmm, he's not trying to have it ready by the wedding? Weird. "Don't you want it done by the wedding?" I ask.

His face is scrunched and puzzled. "I don't care at all," he replies.

I guess he's going to move in with Cassie for a while.

"I've wanted to design a house the way I want it for myself for a long time, and with your advice and opinions, I'm ready to tackle it."

Peter seems so ideal, but I'm surprised he is so inconsiderate of his new bride's preferences. I decide not to get involved with that topic.

I'm reluctant, but actually, I do need the money, and it would be good for me to start a portfolio if I'm thinking about getting back into design.

"Okay," I say. "I'll help you. Is Robby available to help us for the next few weeks?" I still can't believe Cassie is leaving her new house up to Peter, but maybe she knows he's great at this and she isn't. Still, strange.

Peter picks up his phone and texts Robby. Immediately, Robby replies with, "Ready to jump on it."

"I've got to go hit baseballs with a friend, but I'll be back at 10:00," he says, putting his helmet back on and throwing away our coffee cups.

Who hits baseballs at 9:00 in the morning? I start to ask, but Peter changes the subject.

"Let's talk about how much I'm going to pay you," Peter says.

"I would feel more comfortable if you would wait until we are finished," I say, "Then you can pay me what you think it's worth. If I make a few mistakes, then you can take that out of my pay."

"Alright, it's a deal," he says.

"I'm ready to dig in," I say, in shock that I've just agreed to this project. With my mind steeped in recipes for Maggie and now getting ready to seriously and professionally think about Peter's house, there will be little time for me to be in those icky mental Rooms that the Genie doesn't want me to live in.

Hopping back on our bikes, we head to Maggie's. After putting both bikes in Peter's place, I head inside the main house and upstairs to my room.

Getting ready to jump in the shower, I'd first like to text someone to tell them I have two, not just one, new jobs. Who can I tell? Usually I would tell Leland, so who else can I tell? I text Whitney to see if she can talk.

She texts back, "At the park with the kids and some friends. I'll call later."

Okay, I think. Maybe Ellie. I text, "Can you talk for a sec? I've got some exciting news."

I wait and wait. Bubbles are appearing, so she is texting back. But then they go away and don't return. I mean, she doesn't even have time to write that she's so sorry but she's swamped and will call soon.

Okay, let's see. Who else? Not my mother. Not Bailey. Nana doesn't recognize me.

I text my songwriter-stay-at-home-mother friend Crystal with whom I've spent countless hours listening to her talk about trying to make it as a singer-songwriter. "Can you talk a second? I have some good news I want to share about some jobs."

She texts back. "Sure!" I call her. I go through all the info about Maggie and working for Peter, but she keeps interrupting and talking to her toddlers: "Be careful, sweetie, and put the dish nicely on the table. Good job!" and "Bradley, is that nice to take that toy from your sister? Say I'm sorry. That's a good boy."

I'm annoyed that she can't ignore her children for three minutes while I tell her my good news. It's Crystal's turn to express wild enthusiasm for my recent turn of events. After all, I just got dumped by the guy I thought I was going to marry, and I need something positive in my life.

"Darby, this is all so fast. Have you prayed carefully about everything? Do you think maybe you're overreacting since you're so devastated by Leland not wanting to marry you? Shouldn't you lay low for a while instead of turning your life upside down? I remember one time when I was thinking about writing country western music instead of pop music, and I…" and then she waddles into a four-minute tale about something that has nothing to do with my situation.

A thought goes through my head that Crystal is always skeptical of whatever I do. And I'm tired of listening 90 percent of the time to her stuff. She finishes her music story and then resumes talking to her children.

"That's so kind how you put Mrs. Bear next to Baby Bear. Very lovely, Amelia. You're such a nice little mommy." And then she says she has to go because her children are waiting on her to go outside.

And click. Here I am.

The thought that I have absolutely no one to share my good news with cuts like a sharp knife. The realization is brutal. Heartbreaking. I'm terrible at relationships, and no one cares about me. I could die today, and no one would care.

I command myself to Move into Another Room, to think about something else other than my complete failure as a person in relationships. What shall I think about? The heaviness of my failure as a person is spreading its menacing fingers toward me. Move, I say to myself. Change Rooms, I command myself again.

Like pulling an iron ball-and-chain, I take my mind and move it to some ideas for Peter's new house. In five minutes, I have recovered quite a bit and have prevented another fall into the valley of the shadow of despair. What a fight, though. I do recognize, however, that there is a glimmer of hope. I am learning to watch the Parade and start taking control of my thoughts. I wish there weren't so many negative thoughts to take control of.

After showering, I walk into the hall to get some clothes from the extra closet Maggie gave me. I hear Maggie and Peter talking in the kitchen.

"I'm sorry you're having problems," Maggie says.

"I have no idea what to do," Peter says. "I can't believe I'm in this situation."

"I agree, it's difficult," Maggie says.

Even though I'm very curious about Peter's problem, I know I can't ask because it's none of my business. But admittedly, I hope he is realizing he should not be getting married to that terrible, horrible, no good, very bad woman.

Lesson 7

More Rooms to Stay Out Of:
Being Offended, Angry, and Resentful

Still Wednesday, August 29, five minutes later

As I carry my hall closet clothes into my room, I look out my window and see Peter getting into his truck. Again, he is carrying that little baseball bat. Where could he possibly be going? If I get the chance, I'll ask him today.

At 10:00 a.m., Peter and I leave Maggie's as planned to work on the house.

"Are you okay?" I ask, sensing he's not his usual self.

"Not really," he says.

"Do you want to talk about it?" I ask.

His eyes turn to look at me and then back to the road. He's considering what to say.

"It's complicated?" I ask, trying to make a joke.

Without any expression, he says, "Very."

I have no idea what's going on except I heard that small segment of the conversation with Maggie this morning. It's probably about Cassie, and he doesn't want to talk about it with me.

"I've made a mistake," he says. "And now I don't know how to get out of it."

I hope, I hope, I hope he's talking about the Wicked Witch.

"A mistake?" I ask, hoping for more.

"Yes, a mistake—involving a kid," he says.

Could Cassie be pregnant? What is he talking about? Or could this maybe have something to do with that youth baseball bat he's been carrying around?

"I've seen you with a small baseball bat a few times. Is that related?" I ask.

Again, he looks over at me and then back to the road. "Yes, it is."

He pauses and then continues. "What started out as a good idea has not turned out so well," he says. "Maybe I can tell you about it sometime, but not now."

Whatever the problem is, he thinks it's serious. I could hear it in his voice with Maggie, and I can hear it in his voice now.

"You're so easy to talk to that I might tell you too much," he says.

"I'm sorry if I…"

He interrupts, "No, you have nothing to be sorry for. You're one of those people who makes other people comfortable. They open up to you. I like that about you." He looks at me again. "I like a lot of things about you."

Now that was overboard. Engaged people should not talk like that to the opposite sex. They just can't. I'm sure my cheeks have turned a bright pink.

We pull into the driveway, and I quickly jump out of the car. Robby is waiting in the kitchen.

Although I am fairly familiar with demolition, carpentry, plaster and drywall, I am less acquainted with electrical wiring, plumbing, and roofing. Fortunately, Robby and Peter are experts in those areas, so I can focus on what I know. I do like using power tools, and both guys tease me about my industrial-grade goggles and gloves. In front of Peter, Robby says, "Darby, you're a combo of Today's Top Model and Home Improvement. You should have your own cable show."

It's true that I've gotten a lot of attention from guys for my looks, but it fades when they discover how broken I am on the inside. I've struggled with this unmanageable discouragement (and some depression) since I was a teenager. What I want is someone like Peter, but they don't like broken, neurotic girls.

The fear that Robby and Peter will soon discover I'm one of those troubled girls begins to envelop me. But luckily, I hear the Parade and refute it: *Maybe you were broken in the past, but now, with the Genie's help, you are healing. Therefore, maybe your chances to find a good man are not completely gone.* Quickly, I Move into Another Room and focus on my work.

At 3:00, I head back to Maggie's to shower and cook.

Dinner is a wild success again, and after the meal, the same guy corners Peter. This time, Peter quickly escapes to his in-law suite.

After the kitchen is cleaned up, I retreat to my soothing green room. The thought of a glass of wine emerges, but I instantly remember that I'll be glad in the morning if I abstain (the proclamation) even though my Lower Self is pleading for some now. What Room can I Move Into?

Looking at renovation websites is a pleasant alternative, so I grab my laptop and settle down on the chaise lounge. Soon I'm tired and get ready for bed.

Thursday, August 30, 3:00 a.m.

At 3:00 a.m. I awake, thinking about lighting, back splash, and crown molding. I saw some things on my computer before I went to bed, and I've got some new ideas. I think I'll go downstairs and get some red raspberry tea and make some notes before these ideas escape me. Peter says he comes in at 1:00 a.m., and now it's 3:00 a.m., so I feel safe that I won't see him.

Getting my hot tea, I get comfortable on the bar stool in the kitchen and start unloading my ideas onto my legal pad. I can't seem to write fast enough. I'm in such crazy focus that I'm startled when I hear a voice I recognize.

"Can't sleep?" Peter says by way of greeting.

"I thought you came into the kitchen to get a snack at 1:00 a.m.," I say.

"I'm guess I'm on the late shift. I need some cookies." He walks across the kitchen, and in the dim light, I can tell he has on only a pair of gym shorts. His chest is chiseled, as I suspected it would be. He grabs the cookie container from the freezer and sits next to me at the counter.

"What are you doing?" he asks as he leans over to see what I'm writing. His strong arms bump into mine, and he's in no hurry to pull back. His face is very close to mine, too, as he tries to read what I'm writing. I've got as much attraction to Peter as I've ever had to anyone in my whole life. He lights up my whole body.

"Just a few ideas," I say, pulling away. "I'll read them out loud to you." We go through each one but in hushed tones so we won't wake Maggie or her guests.

After positively commenting on several ideas, he changes the subject. "How about another bike ride in the morning?" He is still sitting very close.

"I think I'm going to sleep in," I say.

"If you're going to stay in that same great shape, you've got to keep working out," he says.

Again, this is weird how Peter is engaged yet flirts with women. He certainly shouldn't be talking about my shape.

"You go without me in the morning," I say. "I need my beauty rest."

Quietly, but with full concentration, Peter talks to me as if he's telling me something very serious. "Darby, you don't need any beauty rest. You've got enough beauty for five women."

Why is he doing this? Of course this delights me, but it also puzzles me.

"Thank you, that's nice," I say, and our eyes meet again. What is going on? Why is he stirring me up like this?

"Let's run instead of riding bikes," he says. "I've got a three-mile course mapped out that avoids the rush hour traffic. I've got an early morning errand, so why don't you meet me at 8:00? That gives you plenty of sleep."

I know better. I truly know better. But I'm only human, and I do need the exercise.

"Okay, I'll see you at 8:00," I say, against my better judgment.

He begins to move toward the back door, and I get up to head back upstairs. He said I have enough beauty for five women. These renovation ideas alone could keep me awake, but how do I fall sleep now with Peter Needleman telling me I have that much beauty?

Right before we leave the kitchen, Maggie appears in the doorway. "I didn't know we were having a pajama party," she says.

"The party is over, Aunt Maggie, and you missed it," Peter says. "I'm going to bed. And don't keep my running partner up either. We're running at 8:00 a.m."

I'm embarrassed in front of Maggie for two reasons: I'm downstairs with Peter at night, and I'm running with him in the morning. It must seem very suspicious to her that her engaged nephew and I are meeting in the middle of the night.

Maggie laughs, probably trying to pretend there's nothing improper about our late night rendezvous.

"Good night, you two," she says, as she opens the refrigerator. Then she asks Peter, "Are you taking Cassie to the airport tomorrow?"

"Yes, at 6:30 a.m. before my run with Darby," he says.

Surely she's going to roll her eyes, knowing I'm a temptress.

"Okie-dokie," she says, again not acting like anything is inappropriate.

Confused, I walk up the stairs to my luscious green room. I have two great gigs going, working for Maggie and working for Peter. But I also have one huge mess. I'm letting my thoughts and heart move toward Peter. *Stop it!* I scream to myself. He's not available. Stop it! I shouldn't have agreed to run with him. Finally, I drift off to sleep again.

Still Thursday, August 30, 3 hours later at 6:30 a.m.

I open my phone and see a notification on Facebook that Brad, one of my old boyfriends, has a new post. Knowing better, I click to open it. He's engaged! And to…oh my goodness…it's to a girl in a family I know, and she's only around 22 or 23. When I was a senior in high school, she was in the second grade! And now there she is, all perky and fresh like a ripe peach on a tree ready for the picking, and I'm the old, dry, withered one on the ground.

There's that sorrow again that arrives without permission and just lands on my brain. It's like a thick, muddy glaze that descends. Sure, I have two new jobs I like, but my life still has so many unpleasant situations, especially the fact that I'm aging and drooping, no longer the fresh fruit like Brad's fiancée.

Nothing makes me sadder than Facebook and Instagram. Even though I know everyone posts the best three seconds of their day, it still makes me feel inadequate.

What have I learned to do when this dark cloud descends?

Grabbing my Quartz Journal, I open to the section on my Genius Zone. **But before I can read a word, the Genie appears.**

"Good morning," he says. "Today we are going to continue our lessons on various Rooms to Stay Out Of." He is eating some kind of barley flatbread with a melon on the side. He offers to share, and actually, it is quite tasty.

"In America," I say, "we don't start school before 8:00 a.m., and it's only 6:30." I'm hoping to beg off another intense lesson.

"The sooner you have all the lessons in *Happy School*, the better," he says, ignoring my request. "Today I will teach you about some more Rooms to Stay Out Of, the Rooms of being offended, being angry, and having resentment. We will begin with the Room of being offended."

I'm offended that we're having a lesson at 6:30 a.m.

"If humans begin to pay attention," he says, "they will realize how often they get offended. Their family, co-workers, bosses, employees, friends, and even store clerks regularly offend them."

True. Just yesterday afternoon when I made a manicure appointment, I was offended by the clerk on the phone who rushed me and didn't say goodbye before hanging up.

"A wonderful and life-changing strategy to embrace when offended," he says, "is to see the offense as a dart coming toward you but *not* let the offense land. In other words, you are to *be like smoke* and let the dart of the offense pass through you."

What? Is he saying that I have a choice to *not* be offended? That's idiotic. "How would I ever do that?" I ask. I mean, people do things that upset me all the time.

"As I said," he replies, "you choose to be smoke and let the offense pass through you.[66] You can make this choice, just like you can make the choice to Move into Another Room in Your Brain when WMDs appear in your mind."

I've never heard before that I have a choice to *not* be offended. Pretty radical.[67]

"You will be often offended in life, in small and great ways. But you can learn to be smoke," he says. "This is all about your mind."

My mind. My thinking. My thoughts. Doesn't he have something else to talk about?

"What about this?" I ask, challenging him. "Tell me how to think about this. My sister, Bailey, asked me to babysit this weekend. She has plenty of money, but she likes to use me to save money (because, of course, I don't charge her). I really like my nieces, but I'm offended that Bailey doesn't reciprocate. It's take, take, take."

---

66. "It is his glory to overlook a transgression" (Proverbs 19:11 NASB). There are few things that scripture says are a glory, but one thing is to overlook a transgression. One explanation could be that when we give mercy instead of judgment, we are like God in that moment. This skill or behavior transforms our relationships with everyone we know.

67. Actually, this is not radical at all. For centuries, philosophers and theologians have talked about the virtue and benefits of overlooking offenses.

"That's a great example," he says. "Remember a prior lesson, Lesson 3: Never apply negative interpretations to external situations. Maybe Bailey is afraid to leave her kids with other babysitters. Maybe Bailey likes the influence you have on your nieces. Instead of assuming the worst when you are offended, be careful to examine your interpretation of the situation."

That's absurd. Bailey is merely selfish and cheap.

He goes on. "Just to be clear, I'm not saying you must babysit or always comply with others' requests. You should sometimes set boundaries in inappropriate situations. We will discuss this in our lesson on relationships (Lesson 9). But nevertheless, you can train your mind to not be offended but merely become smoke and let the offense pass through."

I don't know how I would ever do this.

"Here's another example," I say, believing that not being offended would be impossible in this next situation. "When I worked for Jana, she criticized me daily. I was repeatedly offended by her. How should I have handled that?"

"When Jana criticized you, you would have suffered so much less if you had chosen to not be offended and to let the offense pass through. You wasted hours feeling angry that you were mistreated, replaying the scenarios, instead of being smoke (and later, problem-solving). I agree it was good you eventually left that toxic environment, but one cannot always escape a situation."

It calms me just to think about no longer working for Jana.

"Let me give you a third example about my songwriter friend, Crystal," I say. "She talks incessantly about herself and her music. I mean, I'm offended that she turns every conversation into one about her music or her children."

"Friendships are an area we need to explore and dissect in Lesson 9. But for now, when Crystal abruptly or inappropriately turns the conversation to herself, you can choose to let that offense pass through you. It is not the scope of this lesson to discern when to confront and when to overlook, nor is it the scope of this lesson to instruct you how to choose which people are to be in your inner circle. Upon reflection, you may decide Crystal is not a friend to have in your inner circle but maybe only in a larger circle of less intimate friends. But regardless, you must quit being offended so easily. You are making yourself unnecessarily miserable. And the choice to overlook an offense is yours."

Now I'm ready to give him the Big Kahuna. "Genie, what about the way I have been so horribly mistreated by Leland and Bethany? Leland used me for two years. Two vital years! I thought he was going to marry me." My anger rises in my heart as I continue. "And then, to make matters worse, two days after we break up, he starts dating The Girls. I mean, I helped Bethany, my supposed friend, get her stupid job. And they both have humiliated me in front of all of my friends."

The sting returns as I spew out my venom. How I despise Leland and Bethany for doing that to me!

"In large offenses such as the one you experienced with Leland and Bethany, you must go beyond not being offended," the Genie says. "You have to *forgive*. Forgiving and not being offended are, however, close cousins."

"What? Just let them off the hook? That's it?" That is not only impossible, it is undesirable!"[68]

"I'm definitely not saying you have to continue to be in a close relationship with people such as these, but for your part—*your part*—Young Darby, it is imperative that you forgive, that you empty their boxes of offenses, because harboring anger and hate toward others *tarnishes your soul*. The human body was not built to carry anger, resentment, or hate. In fact, science is now revealing that physical harm is done to a person's *health* when they regularly experience anger, resentment, or hate. Remember when we discussed that the *thought* of fear increases your *physical* heart rate? Therefore, I remind you again that *thoughts are things*

---

68. Forgiving will be more thoroughly discussed in *Happy School Advanced*.

and do have a physical effect on your body. You must—and I repeat this with vigor—you must learn to not be offended as well as to forgive. Your very health depends upon it."[69]

"I'm such a piece of work," I sadly admit to the Genie. "In addition to the examples we just discussed, I've got to learn to overlook the offenses of and forgive my mother and so many others. How will I ever learn this?"

"You practice," he says. "When you recognize that you are offended or harbor resentment, you choose—right there—what to do with the thought. You practice this skill of overlooking offenses and forgiving others as you would practice any skill. You will become proficient in time. Being offended and resentful are the default modes that are now written in the software of your mind. But with repetition, you can learn to rewire the software in your brain."

"It seems overwhelming," I say.

"New skills often seem overwhelming at first," he agrees, "but you will see that your emotional health escalates sharply as you practice this skill."

My stomach feels queasy thinking about how many people I am continually offended by and how many people I need to forgive. I realize I am full of resentment.

"Few lessons in life will do more for your relationships as well as your emotional and physical health as learning to overlook offenses and forgiving. We are talking today about extremely high human functioning. Be smoke when you're offended, and empty their boxes of offenses when you are mistreated[70] because bitterness ruins your emotional health. Refuse to cling to hard feelings against anyone. Be a perpetual forgiveness machine."[71]

I don't want to be a forgiveness machine.

---

69. See the parable of the unmerciful servant (Matthew 18:21–25).

70. "Forgive as the Lord forgave you" (Colossians 3:13 NIV).

71. If you've been abused, neglected, or criticized, or if you grew up in a very dysfunctional home, please consider getting some Christian counseling. I recommend forgiving the people who have harmed you and then work with a professional or godly mentor to figure out how to set biblical boundaries.

"Regretfully, I must remind you," he says, "that anger stems from pride—that is, from having blocked goals. Keep in mind that humility and meekness are the antithesis of pride.[72] I am going to Babylon for a vest fitting, but I will be back with another lesson on Rooms that are imperative for you to Stay Out Of." He twirls and disappears.

These lessons are happening too fast. I can't process this much information this quickly. And was he just accusing me of having a problem with pride?

My text message is beeping. Who could this be so early? It's only 7:00 a.m. It's a group text from my friend Ellie, the self-proclaimed secretary of our Sorority Supper Club.

"Good morning, Supper Club. I want to remind everyone that we will meet as usual on the first Tuesday of next month, September 4, which is this upcoming Tuesday night. Let's meet at Stoney River Restaurant at 6:30 p.m. Let me know if you can come, and I'll make reservations."

The texts start coming in. I look for Bethany's text, but it's not there. No big deal because I'm not going anyway. I reply, "Hi, everyone. I'm so sorry, but I'm going to have to take a short hiatus from the group. I have a new job, and I work Sunday through Thursday nights. Sorry to miss. Hope to reconnect soon."

This actually works out great, so now I can avoid any future run-ins with The Girls.

Laying down my phone, I go into the bathroom to get ready for my run with Peter.

In ten minutes, I come back to find my phone has blown up. I have nine messages, and they are all from my Sorority Supper Club friends.

Ellie's message is first: "Hey guys, can everybody meet this Saturday for lunch instead? It won't be the same if Darby is not there. Could we change our regular meeting date to lunch on the first Saturday of the month? Does that work for everyone?"

---

72. Humility vs. pride is discussed in the free online accompanying course, *Happy School Advanced*, available at JulieNGordon.com.

After that, Isabel writes, "I can meet on Saturday for lunch. We want to make this work for Darby." The others chime in and agree.

At the bottom of the group text, Bethany responds. "Sorry, but I can't come this Saturday. Sorry to miss."

No one says much back to her. Apparently, the Supper Club feels like I do about Bethany.

Since she's not coming, I think I will attend. I text back, "You guys are the best. So sweet! I would love to meet everyone for lunch on Saturday. Thank you so much for moving the date."

The texts continue, and we confirm our lunch for noon on Saturday. My friends' willingness to change the meeting time to adapt to my new job schedule is a nice gesture.

I see Peter pull in shortly before 8:00 a.m. after taking Cassie to the airport. We meet outside at 8:00 for our run, as planned.

"I got that done, and I'm ready to run," he says when he sees me.

Got that done? That sounds negative. We start our run at a slow enough pace that I can still talk. "Is everything okay?" I ask. I don't want to be nosey, but we *are* becoming friends.

"I guess so," he says and pauses. Then he adds, "It's just that Cassie wears me out."

I'm not sure what my response to this should be. So I just say, "She does?" giving him an opening if he wants one.

"She's headed to Colorado where we used to live to have her bachelorette party," he says. "All the way to the airport she complained that she wishes the wedding was in Colorado but that she got forced into having the wedding here because Aunt Maggie is paying for so much of it. To me, it's ungrateful."

I don't know what to make of this. I can't believe he's telling me this.

"She's always been somewhat high maintenance, so I shouldn't be surprised," he continues.

Oh my gosh, I think. *Get rid of her! Get rid of her. There's still time.* But of course, I don't say that.

"I'm sorry you're frustrated," is all I can think to say.

"A run is always good for me," he says with a bit of a forced positive attitude. "It's a healthy mood changer. I've already had one cup of coffee, and I'll get another one when we get back. Then I'll immerse myself in our renovation project, and I won't think about it again."

Subconsciously Peter knows how to get himself into another frame of mind by thinking about and doing something else. I don't know how some people just intuitively know this. I have let negative situations turn into negative ruminations for years because I didn't know how to take control of my mind.

On the rest of the run, we talk mainly about the renovation and agree to meet at 10:00 to go to the property.

At 10:00, I meet Peter downstairs, and we drive to the house. It's a hot day, so we set up fans since the new air conditioning system has not yet been installed. Robby meets us there, and the wild work begins. At noon, Peter orders some sandwiches and salads to be delivered to us. The three of us sit on a pile of lumber for about fifteen minutes, resting and eating. The conversation is completely about the renovation.

Wishing I didn't have to stop work at 2:00, I realize I must so I can grocery shop and get ready for dinner tonight. Maybe by next week I'll be more organized with the meals and will only have to shop once or twice a week. But this week, I want to take the group's pulse each night and carefully plan the next evening's dining.

At five minutes before 2:00, Peter says, "It's time for you to leave. I don't ever remember accomplishing this much in four hours in my whole life."

Robby adds, "She can dream it up at the speed of light. Too bad we can only work at the speed of humans."

Clumsily shrugging off the compliments, I gather my things to head back. But I notice my heart is stirred at having my work appreciated. I realize I'm in my Genius Zone. The thought that I've wasted the last ten years of my Genius Zone saddens me, and familiar regret returns. I know I have to move away from this Room of regret, and fortunately, I am now arriving at the grocery store, so that will occupy my mind. I shop and return to Maggie's to prepare a feast.

This evening's meal is the fifth and final meal of the week, and it received another five-star review. Walking into the kitchen with an armload of dishes, Maggie is eager to speak. "Darby, I can't thank you enough. What a week! Five out of five meals have been superb. I feel like a new person with the weight of the evening meal off me."

Peter comes in, too, also carrying dishes from the table. "Is this the last meal of the week? What am I supposed to do for food for the next few of days? I guess there's always grilled cheese."

Maggie and I laugh at Peter as we move quickly around the kitchen to get it back in order.

Such nice people! Both Maggie and Peter are happy, giving, and kind people—so different from my family and the people I've been associated with (like boring Leland, grumpy Jana, and my neurotic mother).

Peter sits on the bar stool as if he's going to stay and chat a little, but the talkative real estate man enters the kitchen, and Peter promptly stands to excuse himself. I'm disappointed but definitely understand.

Before Peter exits, he quietly says, "Darby, tomorrow I'm going to have to take a day off from working on the house."

Even though I'm curious as to why, I decide not to ask. Instead I say, "What about Saturday?"

He turns back around to eye me. "I'll be there, but I don't expect my employees to work on weekends." He pauses and then adds, "You're going to burn out if you keep up this pace."

Ignoring his comment, I say, "I can help you after 2:00 p.m.," thinking of my Sorority Supper Club (now Lunch Club) meeting. "There's so much work to do."

He doesn't smile, but I can detect his pleasure. "Robby is off, but you and I can knock out some work."

Finishing the kitchen, I retreat to my lovely but lonely room. My text message sounds, and I see it's a photo from my sister, Bailey. There's a picture of an elaborate cake that looks like a medieval castle.

"Gracie wants to have a princess party, so here is a picture of the cake she wants for her birthday party Monday afternoon. I know this is short notice, but she couldn't decide on a theme until today. We have invited the fifteen girls from her kindergarten class, along with their mothers."

Gracie is five, and Allie is three, and for the last few years, I have made elaborate birthday cakes for their parties. Bailey always has trouble deciding on a theme, and I have literally spent hours trying to accommodate her wishes for her daughters' cakes.

Reading her text, looking at the elaborate photo, and thinking about having only three days' notice, I start to fume. The outrageous expectations of my sister boil inside as does her lack of reciprocation. Since I'm single, she has adopted my mother's perspective that I have no life and therefore can be imposed upon at any second.

The more I think about it, the angrier I get. That cake will take hours to make, not to mention what it will cost. Bailey never offers to pay, nor does she even hint that the cake is my present. She also expects expensive birthday gifts for her daughters.

As I stew about it, I realize she is completely unconcerned if I have the time or energy to make her stupid cake, only that I do it. I read and reread the text, feeling the self-righteous anger swell in my chest as I think about how wronged I am. Such inconsideration! Such selfishness! Such greediness to not offer to pay! I am offended!

Bailey has plenty of money for everything for her children as well as keeping up her high-priced social status. She spends a fortune on her house and her family's travels. I consistently show up for Bailey and have done so for years, but honestly, I thought she would do something for me occasionally. That's a joke. She just takes advantage of me. I mean, who else would she ask to accomplish this kind of project with only three days' notice?

I know better than to text back when I'm angry, but I don't care. I write, "Bailey, I have two new jobs. I don't see how I could possibly make that cake in three days."

Immediately, I see the bubbles on my text, knowing she is writing back.

"Darby, you make their cakes every year. You knew her birthday was Monday even though we haven't talked about it. Are you working weekends? Sunday? Couldn't you do it over the weekend?"

I start to explain that I don't have a kitchen now, but then I realize she'll offer hers, or worse, Mom's. What do I say? I could spend my entire day off tomorrow working on the cake, but I have other things I need to do: laundry, a hair trim, a dental appointment, and planning Maggie's menus. And then Saturday is booked because I visit Nana in the morning (does Bailey ever go see Nana?) and then go to the College Supper/Lunch Club. And I told Peter I'd help him in the afternoon. I go to church Sunday morning, and then I'll need to shop and cook on Sunday afternoon. I mean, if I wanted to push myself and work on her stupid cake every second, I guess I could, but I don't want to. I'm sick of Bailey imposing on me. She doesn't care what else I'm doing or what I spend.

Before I write back, she adds, "I'm counting on you. Gracie will be so disappointed if she doesn't get this cake. She has her heart set on it."

Oh brother! I'm not sure how to handle this. In the past, I've felt a responsibility to Bailey as my sister, but this feels like I'm being bulldozed. She just wants a fabulous cake to show off to the other moms and their five-year-olds. It doesn't seem fair. Why am I in all of these toxic relationships where people criticize me and impose on me without reciprocation?

I get ready for bed and check my phone. My mother has texted me. "Bailey says you are trying to wiggle out of making Gracie's cake. Surely you're not that busy, are you?"

The thought arises that some wine would numb me from my crazy family, but I remind myself of the proclamation that when I am in my Best Sane Higher Self, I know that alcohol is not what I truly want for my long-term well-being. I make some herbal tea instead and keep thinking about how to handle Bailey.

I decide to send Bailey a text with a compromise.

"Bailey, I've got two new jobs, and I'm super busy. Honestly, I forgot all about Gracie's birthday. If you buy all the ingredients for the cake and go to Hobby Lobby and buy all the decorations for the cake, I can come over from 3 to 6 p.m. tomorrow and make the cake at your house. I have moved and don't have my own kitchen anymore."

She immediately texts back: "I've got both girls with me tomorrow, so how would I ever go to the store and buy the ingredients and decorations? And if you cook here, the kitchen will be a mess. I'm so disappointed, and Gracie will be crushed. I don't know what to do."

Bailey and my mother make me wither like a parched plant. I can't believe what dysfunctional family relationships I have. A mother and a sister should be the source of the richest supportive relationships, yet these are the two that suck me the driest.

Wait a minute. Wait one dadgum minute. What was I just doing? I was allowing myself to feel hugely offended by Bailey. And what else? I was soaking in self-pity like a sponge in dishwater. What did the Genie tell me to do?

First, I'm to be smoke and let the offense pass through instead of letting it land. I think of Bailey's non-reciprocal demands and picture them passing through me like they are darts and I'm smoke. Then, I try to remember what I just learned about self-pity, to not give in to it, to quarantine it and problem-solve. Let's see, what would problem-solving look like?

Pulling out my Quartz Journal, I decide to journal a tad and try to figure out how to handle this. After I briefly write down the scenario and how I feel, I add this:

I do want to have a relationship with Bailey and her girls. I will restate my offer that if she will do the shopping and have everything ready, I will come over to bake and assemble the cake tomorrow from 3:00 p.m. to 6:00 p.m. That's my offer. I can't help it if she refuses.

Grabbing my phone, I text that idea to Bailey, adding, "Let me know if that will work for you."

She texts back, "If that's the best you can do, then I'll have to figure it out. You've always done the cake on short notice before, so this throws me, Darby. But I will try to be ready by 3. This presses me, you know."

She never cares about pressing me. I'm annoyed by her text, but again, I try to be smoke and let the offense pass through me. I've got so much to learn. The Genie said that he would teach me about relationships in Lesson 9. I'm pretty sure I will get an F on the pre-test for that lesson.

What else would the Genie say? He would definitely say to not have self-pity. I certainly could stew about how my sister doesn't reciprocate, but I will choose not to. I will Move into Another Room in My Brain. Seeing a nearby copy of *Traditional Home*, I start scanning the magazine for ideas for Peter's house.

Fifteen minutes later, I realize that instead of diving down into a pity party, I have recovered from the emotional fiasco with Bailey. Bravo! Bravo, indeed! The majesty of watching the Parade March across my Brain and then interrupting it by Hot Potatoes and Moving into Another Room is pretty spectacular. How this truth would have improved my mental health had I known it ten years ago!

And why didn't I know that I could *choose* whether or not to be offended? I can't believe what a dunce I've been about life. There I go again, beating myself up. Let me try to rephrase that with a more optimistic twist. What about, *I didn't know how to think in the past, but I'm glad I'm learning now.*

I laugh at myself for thinking such optimistic thoughts. They are so *not* me.

My mother texts me again: "Can you try to not be selfish this time? The cake is for your little niece, after all."

Although I will try to be smoke and let that offense pass through me for now, I must get some advice about dealing with poisonous, dysfunctional people. I quit my toxic ex-boss, Jana, but I can't just "quit" my mother and sister. However, this level of dysfunction certainly can't continue. I need some principles to live by, some advice, some boundaries, some help. Woe is me, for I am beset by neurotics!

Lesson 8

More Rooms to Stay Out Of: Worry and Fear

Friday, August 31, 6:30 a.m.

It's my day off, but there's no time to relax. I review in my mind all I have to accomplish today—get the oil changed, get my hair trimmed, go to my dental appointment, and then go to Bailey's. Actually, I do enjoy making designer cakes, but it's being with Bailey that is the downer.

Facebook sent me a notification that my friend Crystal has posted something. The temptation is too strong. I click.

It's pictures of Crystal's toddlers in matching smocked outfits. It makes me sad thinking that I don't have any children and that maybe I never will.

One problem I suffer from is that I compare myself with other people. I compare myself with the women who have what I want, so of course, that makes me feel disappointed. I have to remember that I only want a *few* things they have, not *everything*. For example, I would hate (all caps HATE) being married to Crystal's boring husband. I can't imagine listening to him talk at supper for the rest of my life. He brags about his job (the business his dad built) and his money like he's Elon Musk. I couldn't take it. (But look at me judging Crystal when I was getting ready to marry boring Leland.)

Walking to my bay window, I notice there are screens on the windows. I open a window to let some of the outside world in. For some reason, this makes me sad, too. The beautiful trees, the warm air, the birds' noises, all of it highlights the fact that I don't really have anything I like much in my life except a couple good jobs, and who knows how long they will last?

I still don't know what to do about these family members who drive me crazy. And although my Sorority Supper/Lunch Club did change the time so I could come, they never ask me over because they're always getting together as *couples*. Couples, couples, couples. What a horrible word to a spinster.

Maybe my friends have changed a dinner to a lunch when I can attend, but they still don't show me much attention, appreciation, or admiration. In fact, they are consumed with their own little worlds, apparently giving no thought to mine.

Another awful thing is that I'm in major debt, and my father's inheritance is dwindling. I kept spending because I thought Prince Leland and his ophthalmic salary would rescue me. Oh sure, my little job at Maggie's is fun, but honestly, it's a drop in the bucket compared to what I spend.

So many people seem able to get up and go about their lives with contentment, but not me. I wake up, and the disappointments of the world press in. One cup of coffee barely helps; I need three or four. And even then, my mind swims in disappointment.

What did I just think? I just heard my mental Parade. My relentless, negative, self-pitying Parade!

I don't think there's any hope that the Genie could ever help someone as messed up as I am, someone with such deep grooves of negativity. What am I to do when this mountain of discouragement collapses on top of me? For one thing, I know I must shed this self-pity. I'm just now even recognizing that I have it!

Quarantining helps a lot. Moving into Other Rooms in My Brain helps, too. I've got to get busy with something to keep my mind occupied.

Maggie's guests have all checked out, and the bed-and-breakfast will be empty until Monday. (It's Labor Day weekend, so the guests will arrive a day later than usual.) Maggie has a cleaning service come every Friday, and she said it was fine if they cleaned my room and bath, too. I have never been very fond of housework.

Getting ready to exit Facebook, I notice the next post is Bethany's, and she has added a picture of Leland and her in his den. I command my brain to Move into Another Room. I close my phone and head downstairs, gathering my laundry to take with me.

"Good morning, Darby," Maggie says, sipping coffee at the breakfast bar. "Would you like some breakfast?"

"Yes, I would," I say. "I think I'll scramble some eggs."

Getting what I need out of the fridge, Maggie chats again about the great week of cooking, her new lowered stress, and how she enjoys having me around. All of the much-appreciated praise pours encouragement into my brain.

Then she adds, "It looks like you and Peter have become good friends."

Uh oh. Here comes the talk where she tells me what a temptress and intruder I am, and although she likes me, I'm fired.

"I've been rather worried about being with Peter so much," I say. "I'm sorry, and I…"

"What on earth are you talking about?" she interrupts. "I'm glad you are helping Peter with his house. What could possibly be wrong with that?"

She knows about the bike rides, the runs, and the 3:00 a.m. pajama party in the kitchen. Is she going to ignore all of that? I feel so guilty for enjoying the company of an engaged man.

"Peter was such a sweet little boy," Maggie continues, "and now he's turned into a hard-working, compassionate, and honest young man. My sister was so proud of him."

"It's sad she's missing the wedding," I say.

"Oh my, how she would have loved to be at this wedding," Maggie says, and I sense her emotional depth. "My sister said the hardest part of cancer and dying was that she knew she was never going to see any of her grandchildren. I think that's why I participate as much as I do because I know it would make her happy."

Maggie is simply one of the most thoughtful people I know. I can't believe I'm in a relationship with her again. I decide to be a little honest.

"Maggie, I hope you think I'm appropriate with Peter. I mean, I'm working for him so I have to be with him."

She looks directly at me. "Of course you're appropriate with him. I don't know what you're talking about. You've always been a very nice girl and extremely appropriate. You and Peter both have high moral standards."

Well, I had to get that out. She can't see inside my heart, the way I long for him, but there's no need to tell her that. He will be married soon, and then I will draw the line. No more exercising or hanging out with him then.

At 3:00 p.m., I arrive at Bailey's, and she is unusually stressed. You would think she was running the United Nations and had the pressure of the next World War on her shoulders. But her stress is over the decorations for the birthday party, the flowers in the front beds looking right for her guests, and the food she will serve her five-year-old guests and their mothers.

Bailey purchased all the supplies, so I get to work. First, I bake the cakes, the castle's foundation. Then I prep the icing and add the appropriate food coloring. With the icing and all the plastic toy pieces Bailey purchased, I create quite an extravagant castle. As I put the finishing touches on the cake, my niece, Gracie, is joyously dancing around and clapping her hands.

Bailey doesn't say much about the extravagance of the cake, but I can tell she wants to say something.

"Darby, I want to talk to you about putting Nana in a nursing home," she says.

I'm not in the mood for this conversation, so I try to end it quickly. "Nana was very specific years ago that she wanted to stay in her apartment as long as possible and not go to a nursing home."

"Maybe she did," Bailey counters, "but she probably didn't realize it would cost over $100,000 a year to have caregivers come in to take care of her. She's demented now, and she won't know the difference."

Demented and won't know the difference? I feel my anger rise. I have visited Nana every Saturday for fifteen years, and I think Bailey goes twice a year. At Christmas a few years ago, there was an open house at Nana's apartment complex, and Nana wanted Bailey to come with her baby (she only had one then). But Bailey said the time of the open house conflicted with Gracie's nap, and of course, she didn't go. It's pathetic how little she truly cares about Nana. This is all about the inheritance.

Hearing the back door open, I suspect it's Bailey's husband, Daniel. My stomach drops as I turn and see my mother. She has the usual accusatory look on her face.

"Well, well, it's the daughter who never calls her mother, who never tells her mother what's going on, who takes new jobs and moves without telling her mother," she begins. "Darby, I don't know how you can treat me this way."

Feeling the tsunami begin to stir, I try to calm myself. "Mom, I'm going to start calling you twice a week instead of every day. I will call you when I can talk. It's the best I can give you right now since I'm working two jobs."

She ignores what I just said and sits down on a bar stool so she's right in front of me. "Darby, I want to talk to you about Nana."

Oh, I see. I should have known it was my mother who was stirring up Bailey.

"You have her Power of Attorney, and I want to know how much money she has," she says, as though she has a perfect right to this information.

This is how she treated me when I was a child, giving me orders to obey. I now know that as an adult, she doesn't get that kind of power over me.

Then Bailey chimes in, "And I want to know about the will."

The fact that I'm getting 50 percent of the inheritance, that Bailey is only getting 25 percent, and that Nana's church is getting the other 25 percent is going to be a volcanic explosion similar to the one at Mount St. Helens.

"I don't think Nana wants me to talk about that," is all I can say.

My mother is never easily dissuaded. "Darby, Nana is eating up her savings with that round-the-clock help, so we need to put her in a nursing home. What happens when she runs out of money? Who's going to pay for her care then? You?"

I definitely don't tell her that Nana could easily live another ten years on her money before it runs out.

My silence tells my mother something. "Oh, there must be a lot of money because you aren't worried about her running out of money," she snarls. "She's like a vegetable now, so it doesn't matter if she goes into a nursing home."

My little nieces are listening to their calloused, cold-hearted grandmother. She's setting a terrible example. A combination of sadness and anger overwhelm me that this is my family of origin. I need the Genie's lesson on handling toxic relationships.

"Mom, I am not telling you how much money Nana has. And she is going to stay in her home with round-the-clock help as long as I have her Power of Attorney."

"I want to hear about the inheritance, Darby," Bailey jumps back in. "Do I get half?"

Knowing there's going to be a nuclear fallout when the will is read, I decide I had better soften that blow now. "Bailey, actually you're not. You get a lot, but not half," I say.

With a shriek, she adds, "And you? Do you get half? Do we get the same?"

Maybe I shouldn't have said anything. "I get a little more, Bailey, but really, I'm the one who has been close to her for years."

"That doesn't matter with inheritance," she shouts back. "I should get the same. Pitiful! Just pitiful!"

Why did I bring that up? Oh dear. "Guys," I say, "it's really not good for my mental health to have these kinds of confrontations. So just to let you know, I'm not going to talk about Nana's money again."

"Oh! So now you are accusing us of disturbing your mental health?"

my mother says like she's offended. "I've had about enough of this." She hastily grabs her purse and heads for the door.

"Mom, you don't have to go," I say calmly. "I'm getting ready to leave, so you can stay and visit with Bailey."

My mother throws her hands into the air. "You are so touchy, Darby, and such a prima donna who thinks you can do whatever you want."

"Happy birthday, Gracie," I say as I walk toward the back door. There's so much tension that even my little nieces are frozen like statues. I walk out the door and sense that a panic attack is coming.

Getting in my car, I drive toward Maggie's house. When my whole body begins to shake, I know a mild panic attack is at hand. I am glad, however, that I stood up to my mother's bullying about Nana. My mother is one fierce rattlesnake when it comes to money.

It's unimaginable to me that anyone could be so hard-hearted as my mother and Bailey. The disappointment in who they are washes over me again. However, I will *not* tolerate them abusing Nana.

Maggie has gone somewhere, and so has Peter, so I'm alone in the house. The thought of having a glass of wine to dial down my emotional turbulence comes to mind, but the memory of the proclamation quickly dispels that idea. I grab some leftovers from the fridge, take a long bath, organize some clothes, start a new novel I purchased on Amazon, and spend an hour on social media before turning in early.

In the middle of the night, I hear banging outside my window. A woman with a Spanish accent is saying "Pee-ter! Pee-ter!"

I throw back my covers and run to the window, which has a great view of Peter's suite. In the moonlight and with the glow from the street lamp, I can see a woman with thick, long, dark hair. She has dark skin and a J Lo behind. She is dressed in tight, white jeans with a tight tank top that's revealing quite a cleavage.

A little boy, probably around seven years old, gets out of the car and starts walking toward Peter's door.

"Trev-vor! Trev-vor! I told you to stay in the car. Get back in the car.

Now! Now!" says the Latin beauty.

The little boy backs up as she points to the car.

Then Peter comes out. I don't know what she's saying, but she's upset and talking nonstop, mostly in Spanish but sometimes in English. Peter doesn't say much, but she is letting him have it about something. Trevor gets out of the car again and starts walking toward the door.

"Hey, Buddy," Peter says to him in a warm and friendly voice.

"Trev-vor! I told you! Get back in the car! Now!" He doesn't move. She walks toward him, and he runs back to the car.

She returns to Peter's door and starts crying, speaking now in a highly emotional manner. I watch it for a long time.

Finally, she throws her hands in the air and says, "It's not fair to me or Trev-vor." Then she slams her car door and drives off hurriedly. Peter slowly shuts his door, and that seems to be the end of it.

As I lie back down in the dark, I try to figure out what that scene was all about. Surprised, I get a text message. It's from Peter. "Did that wake you up?"

"Yes, but I don't mind. It sounded upsetting."

"It was. Can you meet in the kitchen?"

"Sure. See you in 5 minutes."

Quickly, I throw on a sweatshirt, add two strokes of mascara to each eyelash, and put on some quick, natural-looking blush and lipstick. When I get to the kitchen, Peter is already on the bar stool with his head in his hands.

I get some water and crawl up on the bar stool next to him. "I'm sorry because I can tell how unfriendly that conversation was," I say.

"It's all such a mess," he says, "a colossal mess."

I don't ask any questions but just sit there and wait for him to explain.

"When I moved here, I met Andressa," he says. "We started dating a little bit. Then I began to play sports with her son, Trevor. She wanted Trevor to take piano lessons, and I gave her some money so he could. And then she wanted him to take taekwondo lessons, and again, I agreed to pay. I knew I was going down a dangerous road, but I did it anyway."

I don't say a word, and I don't move my gaze from him. He still hasn't looked at me.

"I knew early on that I wasn't going to marry Andressa. I also knew it would be better to go ahead and break it off. But since I was new to Memphis and didn't know anyone else, I let things keep going."

This was pretty stupid of Peter, but let him who is without sin cast the first stone.

"Then, when I was finally ready to break up, Andressa told me she lost her job. So I thought I'd wait until she got another job. I helped out a little by buying them some groceries and helping with the rent, thinking she was trying to get another job."

"That sounds reasonable," I say, trying to say something helpful.

He shakes his head. "But I found out she *quit* her job. And she wasn't even trying to find another one. I just can't believe I let myself get involved with this. Even though we broke up, I continued to give her money so Trevor wouldn't suffer. Such poor judgment on my part."

I agree. I so agree. I wonder how Cassie plays into this, but I definitely don't ask.

"Yesterday, I went over to tell her I couldn't give her any more money and that I would not be able to spend time with Trevor anymore—although that grieves me and that's another entire subject. So then tonight, after drinking too much, she comes over and bangs on my door."

"I can see why you're upset," I say, thinking of Cassie and the upcoming wedding. I can't believe how men can be such dunces.

"I told her tonight I would give her money for two more months, but that would be the end and she would have to figure out something else."

I wait, and he continues.

"If this had just been about Andressa, I would have pulled back a long time ago. But when I tried to pull back before, Andressa told me that Trevor was crying in his bed at night because he missed me."

Peter shakes his head. "This was just incredibly bad judgment on my part. Incredibly stupid. I was blind to not see how this would all play out."

"Does Cassie know any of this?" I ask.

"Cassie? Are you kidding me? She's the last person I would ever tell any of this to," he says in a forceful voice.

They certainly don't have much of an intimate relationship.

"Andressa is very beautiful," I say.

"Yes, she is beautiful," he admits, "but beauty loses its shine when the character is severely flawed."

We both get up to go back to bed. "See you tomorrow," he says. "Thanks for listening."

"Goodnight," I say. "I'm sorry you have to deal with this."

Getting back into bed, drowsiness returns, and I quickly fall asleep.

Saturday, September 1, 7:00 a.m.

Waking up, I check my phone. No messages or calls, so I click on my news app. Scrolling down, I see a story about the fun summer the Royal children had this year. Clicking on the story, my heart drops as their lives look perfect. Then I think of my life as an old maid.

I think about the time wasted on Steve, on Brad, on Rich, and now, worst of all, on Leland, and I feel even worse. Of course, I now see the many mistakes I made and the numerous things I did wrong. There are so many things I would do differently. Why, if I had the chance to do it over, I would…

Stop! I say to myself. Hot Potatoes! I catch myself rerunning my Failure Movies in my mind. That is not helpful, the Genie told me, after I've mined the situation for what to learn, which I've done a thousand times. It's time now to quarantine those failures. I am not allowed to ruminate on them or allow them to walk in and sit down in the living room of my mind. I must move into another Room in My Brain. What can I think about?

Before I can think of something, the Genie appears. Naturally, he picks another bad time.

"Today's lesson will be brief as I must leave for a sale in Turkey on turban gems." He makes himself comfortable and hands me my Quartz Journal, obviously expecting me to take notes. "Our lesson today will be on still more Rooms to Stay Out of, namely the Rooms of worry and fear."

I'm going to take a beating from this lesson.

"Humans vary greatly in their tendency to worry," he says. "When the optimists in life get fired, they are excited about the opportunity to start fresh and anew. In contrast, pessimists are certain that a headache is a brain tumor."

I've often wondered if my headaches could be brain tumors.

"First, I will explain some general information about worry and fear," he says. "Then I will follow with practical suggestions on how to overcome these enemies."

These lessons are coming like missiles, and I can't process everything fast enough.

"As you know, not all worry and fear are bad," he says. "Humans need to be afraid of danger such as a fire. But humans often excessively worry about relationships, money, health, children, and many other subjects."

He left out singleness.

"The key point to understand, Young Darby, is that humans see their external circumstances as the *cause* of their worries. But they are not. The cause of their worries and anxiety is their *thought patterns*. Worry is caused by worrying *thoughts*."

There he goes again, attributing everything to the mind.

"Worry happens," the Genie says, "when the mind projects itself into the future and imagines something going wrong. Worry amplifies a situation and often turns it into a catastrophe. Remember how we talked about 'awfulizing' in Lesson 2?"

I remember the lesson, but that doesn't mean I quit doing it.

"When you worry excessively," he says, "it is as if your thoughts are stuck running through an endless repeat cycle. But you can *interrupt* those anxious thoughts and break the loop. As I've taught you during our *Happy School* course, you can quarantine thoughts that make you worry and think about them during one of the three problem-solving times. Play Hot Potatoes. Be smoke, and let worry pass through you. Then Move into Another Room in your Brain and think about something else. Your greatest weapon against worry is your ability to think another thought."

He keeps saying that my greatest weapon is to think another thought. It's a little harder than he suggests.

"As you learn to repeatedly interrupt anxious thoughts, you will develop new neural grooves in your brain," he says.

New schoolyard paths, I remember.

"Determine if your worry is possibly solvable," he says. "If it is, brainstorm solutions in your Quartz Journal. Research, think, plan, and take action to solve your problems. But at the end of that session, you must again quarantine your thoughts."

Quarantine, quarantine. He says the same things.

"If your particular worry is *not* solvable, you will need to work on the principle of acceptance and begin to understand and accept the uncertainty of life."[73]

I suppose my singleness is *possibly* solvable.

"The most important fact you need to know," he says, "is that once again, you are not the *victim* of your anxiety but the *producer* of it. By listening in on the Parade of Thoughts that March across Your Brain, you will be able to discern the thoughts that you are having so you can refute, replace, or reframe them. Now, let's move on to a few concrete ideas to reduce your anxiety."

Let's.

"The first practical suggestion is to remember the huge ability of exercise to affect your brain chemistry," he says. "Exercise literally changes the

---

73. In *Happy School Advanced,* I will have much to say about accepting difficult, unsolvable circumstances.

brain because of the hormones produced when exercising. Take a walk, water your flowers, or ride a bike. Increasing exercise is the first prescription anyone should try if they are plagued with worry or anxiety."

I know this, but I often forget it.

"The second practical suggestion is to address one's diet," he says. "Sugar and processed carbs are notoriously detrimental to your emotional state, as is alcohol."

I gave up sugar a year ago, and I hope my new resolution about an alcohol-free lifestyle will eventually help my hormones reset.

"A third suggestion that diffuses anxiety is one, of course, you know, and that is talking to a trusted friend who will listen without criticizing you. Lesson 9, as I've said, will be about relationships, and I will discuss friendship further then."

Friends who will listen? That's a rare commodity.

"A fourth suggestion to combat worry is laughter because laughter is a great calming tool," he says. "Laughing with others is the best medicine, but watching funny podcasts, shows, or clips is helpful, too."

This is another suggestion I was already familiar with but usually forget. I remember how as a teenager I used to read the cartoon series *Calvin and Hobbes* when I was upset with my life. The cartoons got my mind thinking about something else. I never made the connection, though, that I was changing Rooms in My Brain.

"And probably the best tool for handling anxiety is prayer,"[74] he says. "Prayer and meditation actually change structures in your brain."

"What about drugs?" I ask. "Should I get some prescription medicine for my anxiety?" I've been considering getting some again.

"Medication provides only short-term relief and usually has side effects," he says. "What is essential is that you look at the root of your anxiety: your thoughts."

I knew he wasn't going to recommend pharmaceuticals.

---

74. The amazing, fabulous, life-changing power of prayer! *Happy School Advanced* has much to say on this topic.

"Nutrition, as you know, is non-negotiable for mental health," he says. "It is beyond the scope of *Happy School* to discuss nutrition in detail, but hopefully, you will pursue knowledge in this area."

I do enjoy studying nutrition.

"Just to be clear, Young Darby, unless you're facing imminent physical harm, worry and fear are just bad management of your mind," he says.

He can't be serious. Not worry? This course is not for ordinary humans. "You are doing superb in *Happy School*," he says. "I know you'd like to experience complete emotional freedom, but not only have you not had all the lessons, but it will take months of daily practice before you are proficient (remember the piano analogy?). I will return shortly for the important lesson on relationships," and he swirls like smoke from an extinguished candle and disappears.

If the Genie could read minds, he would know I'm doing terrible in *Happy School*. Well, maybe not terrible, because at least I'm not drinking alcohol. Writing out a Best Sane Higher Self proclamation was what I needed to have handy so I could talk back to myself at the point of the craving and ambush.

I jump in the shower to get ready for my busy day ahead. I want to get an early start and go see Nana before the Sorority Supper/Lunch Club today. And then, of course, I'm meeting Peter at his house this afternoon.

When I get to Nana's apartment, Ernestine, her caregiver, is putting a little makeup on Nana.

"Nana, you look so pretty," I say, looking at her white hair and rosy cheeks.

"Thank you," she says, though it's obvious she doesn't recognize me.

"And your pearl necklace looks so nice," I add. Nana still likes to get completely dressed, although she rarely sees anyone other than her caregivers and therapists who come to her apartment.

"Your Nana sure remembers her jewelry," Ernestine jokes, "even though she can't remember her granddaughter." We laugh, and I think how much I like and trust Ernestine.

"I don't want to cause any trouble, Darby," Ernestine says cautiously, "but this morning when I was in your grandmother's safe looking for her pearl necklace, I noticed that her diamond stud earrings were not in there."

Ernestine looks down as if she's not sure she should tell me this.

"Where do you think they are?" I ask. My mind starts racing. Ernestine along with another caregiver named Nykia and a third caregiver named Rosie are the only three who know the combination to the safe—the only three besides Bailey, that is. Ernestine, Nykia, and Rosie have been working for Nana for years, and they are all as trustworthy as gold. I know they didn't steal the earrings.

"Do you have any ideas?" I ask.

Again, Ernestine looks down. "I don't like to accuse people of anything," she says.

"Ernestine! What are you thinking? Please, you have to tell me."

"Well, again, I'm not accusing anyone," she says, "but Bailey did visit last week, and she was alone in the bedroom with the safe."

That's ridiculous, I think. Bailey is a brat, not a thief. Ernestine continues, "I've known Nykia and Rosie for about ten years, and I'd bet my life it wasn't them."

I agree, but I can't imagine it was Bailey. "Is it possible Nana wore them and maybe took them off herself and placed them somewhere?"

"I guess it's possible," she says. "But I'm very careful about your grandmother's nice jewelry, and I know Nykia and Rosie are, too."

I don't say anything, but I'm confident they will turn up. No one stole those earrings.

Nana and I have our usual chat as I massage her arms with body lotion. Today I also paint her fingernails, which she especially enjoys.

After saying goodbye, I drive to the Stoney River Restaurant to meet my friends. On the way, I call Bailey.

Bailey answers. "Hi, Darby. Gracie can't quit talking about the cake you made for her. She loves it."

"I'm glad," I say, feeling good that I made the effort to squeeze in the time to make it.

"I can't talk," I say, "but I wanted to ask you a question. Nana's diamond studs are missing from her safe. Do you know anything about that?"

Not hesitating, she replies, "Oh, Darby, I bet one of her caretakers stole them. You know how caretakers are when no one is looking."

I'm appalled by her comment. It is a horrible thing to say.

"Ernestine, Nykia, and Rosie have been working for Nana for years, and they've never even taken a pencil. I can't believe it was them," I say.

Raising her voice, she declares, "Well, I bet it was. They act so goody-goody and then do something deceitful like this. It happens all the time."

I wanted to say, "No it doesn't," but I let it slide.

"I'm sure they didn't take them," I say, defending the three. "I guess Nana took them out when no one was looking and put them somewhere. I bet they show up."

"They'll show up," she readily agrees. "Nana has lost her mind."

Again, I didn't like her response. Why does she have to say things like "Nana has lost her mind"? It's unkind and unnecessary.

"Well, have a good time at your party on Monday," I say. "Send me a picture. I can't be there, as I said, because I'm working at that time."

"Sure, I'll send you one. Bye, Darby." Click. She doesn't even wait for me to say goodbye. Be smoke, I tell myself, and allow the offense to pass through.

Continuing my drive toward the Stoney River Restaurant, I notice that I feel a little social anxiety. I mean, what is that about? I've known all these people for years, and The Girls said she couldn't be there. Feelings come from thoughts, the Genie says, so what thoughts are creating this anxiety?

Maybe the anxiety is from thinking I'm defective since everyone else is married with kids. And then there's me, the pitiful, perennial single.

Whoa! I just heard *that* negative Parade. Let's see, what am I supposed to do? Refute it? With what? It seems true to me. I laugh at myself and realize what a stubborn case I am.

Okay, I'll try again. Refuting it would mean I would say to myself, *The past does not predict the future. Just because I've had failure before doesn't mean I can't figure this out and turn things around. One's marital state does not denote a person's worth. I can't expect these friends to understand the unique path the Creator has me on.*

What else can I say to myself? Maybe I can *assign another interpretation* to my circumstance of being an old maid. What about, *Although I am not married, it might be because the right person has still not crossed my path.*

It's actually kind of funny hearing myself say things I don't really believe. But refuting and assigning other interpretations definitely makes me feel better. And actually, my new interpretation *could* be true.

I do like these friends (except The Girls, and she's not coming), so I should have a good time.

Walking into the Stoney River Restaurant, I'm apparently a little late. It looks like I'm the last one to get here. There are only two seats left, so I take one of them.

Everyone is chatting about their weekend plans with their husband and children. I try to enter in and be interested, but I can't help noticing that their topics are not mine. For example, the topics are the best pre-schools, good resale events on designer toddler clothes, and anniversary destinations. What I thought would be a restoring time with friends has instead caused my WMDs to rain like cats and dogs.

And to make matters worse, Bethany—who sent an RSVP that she was *not* coming—walks through the door. Bethany has straggly hair that always looks like it needs to be cut. As usual, she has on trashy clothes. She always shows her breasts, and her clothes look ridiculous, if you ask me. If Leland's mom didn't like me, she will jump out of her skin when she meets Bethany.

The table gets quiet since everyone knows she swooped up Leland right under my nose. It's pretty daring to show up in a group when you just snaked a member's boyfriend. Everyone is holding their breath for my reaction. But honestly, ten days out from the breakup, I've got my mind thinking it was actually a good thing. I didn't really love Leland, and now I've been spared a lifetime of boredom.

"I hope it's okay that I didn't RSVP," she mutters. "I didn't know until the last minute if I was going to be free."

That's a total lie, but no one confronts her.

The table is still quiet as she takes the only vacant chair left—next to me.

Crystal directs a question directly to me, ignoring Bethany. "Darby, tell us about your new jobs."

My stomach is in knots, but I pretend and put on a stoic face. "I'm cooking five days a week at a bed-and-breakfast, but it's to feed the owner's guests *at night* during the week." I then explain the unusual setup at Maggie's and add, "I've also been hired by someone to help them renovate an old house."

This group is big-time into renovating old houses, and they want to know which house, who I'm doing it with, and more. I wish we could get the spotlight off of me. My stomach almost feels nauseous.

Bethany gets a phone call and says, "Excuse me, I've got to take this." She gets up from the table and goes out in the hall. When she's out of earshot, Crystal says, "I think it's rude of her to come since she knows she's dating your ex." The rest of the table moans in agreement.

Then Bethany comes back to the group. "I'm sorry, but something's come up, and I'm going to have to leave. Can you please cancel my order?" With that, she picks up her purse.

Quietly and with no enthusiasm, a few people mutter, "Bye, Bethany." No one says anything else to her.

"Why did we let her join this group?" Crystal asks. "She's so inappropriate."

No one else says what they're thinking quite like Crystal. Everyone else raises their eyebrows, but no one else chimes in. These are nice girls, and they know it's wrong to gossip, so they are trying not to participate.

But secretly, everyone is enjoying the drama.

The spotlight returns to me. "Darby, are you okay?" Crystal asks. "How are you handling *things*?"

I hate this. What do they want me to say? *I'm doomed to be a childless spinster, but it's fine. Let's keep talking about the best pediatrician in town.*

I answer with the truth. "I'm really fine. I knew Leland wasn't right for me, but I just let the relationship go on. This is actually good for me."

Ellie chimes in, "Oh, I love your positive attitude. That's what you have to do in these hard situations, convince yourself that *what you have* is best."

I think she meant well, but it came off as, *You're devastated that you lost another boyfriend but you are pretending to be positive about it.* That's not really true in this case, as I really am glad to be free of Leland. I just want this conversation to end.

During the rest of the lunch, I try to ask questions and listen attentively. Naturally, everybody is more than happy to talk about their pregnancies, their husband's new business venture, their children's cute words, and their wonderful, perfect lives.

As I walk out the door of the restaurant, I feel tremendously downcast.

But then, as I'm fastening my seatbelt, I remember the magic. Move into Another Room in my Brain. Although I don't have a wonderful husband or adorable babies, I do have two jobs I like, and I'm going to work at one of them right now. I command myself to think about the afternoon's work and quarantine the Supper/Lunch Club's luncheon.

When I arrive at the house, Peter is already there, cleaning the wall where we will work together to install a tile backsplash. We apply the tile adhesive, attach the tiles, and then apply the grout. Mostly we work, but Peter finds time to tease me, and occasionally, I feel him staring at me.

At 5:00, Peter declares it's quitting time since it's Saturday. I leave first and head back to Maggie's.

While I'm making some tea in Maggie's kitchen, Peter comes in the back door. After some initial small talk about the day's work on the house, he asks, "Are you busy tonight?"

What lie can I make up? It's such an imposition to try to act like I have a social life. I might as well admit that the Old Maid is home alone.

"Uh, no, I'm not," I say. I'm ready to add some things I might work on tonight, but he speaks up first.

"Want to meet me here in the kitchen in a little while and play Sequence?" he asks.

I know Cassie is out of town, but I don't think he should be playing games with other women while she's gone.

Maggie walks in and hears Peter. "Oh, Sequence is such a good game, Darby. Do you know how to play?"

I don't get these two. It doesn't seem right.

"No, I don't know how," I say. Thinking it would be alright if Maggie joined us, I add, "Are you going to play, too?"

"No," she says. "I'm having dinner with a friend tonight. But you should learn how to play."

Then turning to Peter, she says, "She has a quick mind, Peter, so you'd better bring your best game."

Peter turns to me with a straight face. "What if I meet you downstairs in an hour? Best two out of three games wins. And the loser cooks dinner for the winner."

Maggie laughs. "Peter will certainly be bringing his top game now, so you'll be cooking tonight, Darby." Maggie leaves to go to her room.

I'm still a little stunned that Maggie doesn't think it's wrong for me to be with Peter. Some people are okay with different-sex friendships, but I have always been suspicious of the male-female chemistry. But if Maggie thinks it's okay for me to hang out like this with Peter, I am certainly glad to have something to do.

"Sounds like fun," I say. "See you at 6:15?"

There is that expressionless look on Peter's face again. "At 6:15, the contest commences," he announces.

Walking upstairs, I realize that Peter needs dinner, and he's rather certain he can beat me at Sequence and, hence, get dinner. How stupid of me to think this was possibly about me.

Quickly I shower and wash my hair. Although I merely wear jeans and a T-shirt, I do carefully put on my makeup and curl my hair. I even use a little of my red lipstick. I feel the tiniest bit guilty using red lipstick, but I do it anyway.

Peter is already at the kitchen table with the board game out when I get downstairs. Seeing me, he remarks, "I didn't know I was going to play with this year's *Bachelorette* contestant. Your hair is curly. I like it."

I'm a little embarrassed because it's obvious I put some effort into how I look, but a girl is allowed to wash and curl her hair, right?

Peter explains the rules, and we begin. He wins the first game, but I'm concentrating, and soon I'm catching on to the strategy. I win the second game.

When I play the winning card to win the last game, he looks at me with a straight face. "Maggie warned me about your brain, but I didn't think you'd learn that fast. Okay, I guess I'm the cook. Let's see what's in this fridge to cook."

He opens up the refrigerator doors and stares.

"What about eggs Benedict?" he asks. I start laughing because I think he's kidding.

"No, seriously," he says. "There's Canadian bacon in here, and I know how to make a quick and easy Hollandaise sauce in the blender."

"Sounds delicious," I say. "Should I assist the chef and steam some broccoli?"

"All help is appreciated," he says, and starts opening the cupboards looking for pans.

Of course, I end up helping, and the entire meal is delicious.

During dinner, Peter's text message goes off, and he pulls his phone out of his pocket. "Excuse me," he says, and sends back a text. He puts his phone back in his pocket, and I don't say anything.

We are both silent. "It was Andressa," he finally says. "She wanted to know if I would give her money for three months instead of two. I wrote back and told her 10 weeks. That way, it seems like we've reached a mutual agreement since we negotiated. I want to do this as gently as possible because of Trevor."

I still don't say anything and wait.

"I don't know what to do about Trevor," Peter says, with obvious discomfort. "His father abandoned him, and now he's going to feel like I did."

Peter is holding his face in his hands like he was last night when we talked about this same subject. "When I first started dating Andressa," he says, still looking down, "I really liked her because, of course, she was careful to hide all her warts. But then when I started seeing who she really was, I was attached to Trevor. When I broke up with Andressa the first time, I asked her if I could continue a relationship with Trevor. She went ballistic. She said if I wanted access to Trevor, I would have to date her exclusively and help support them. Now I feel like I've harmed Trevor by getting close to him and then withdrawing. I hate that I've harmed Trevor by my poor judgment."

Peter continues. "I've asked Andressa and Trevor to forgive me, but I'm still plagued by the fact that I've hurt the little guy."

Finally, I decide to speak. "It seems to me that you are trying to do the best you know how to do. You're a human, and humans make mistakes."

I learned that from the Genie.

I continue, "We all make mistakes. But you can't let regret beat you up indefinitely. We have to try to make amends the best we can, and then we have to move on."

He looks up at me like he wants me to say more.

"Now you've got to forgive yourself," I say. I dole out this advice like I'm some kind of expert, but truthfully, I'm still trying to forgive myself for being so stupid about all the wrong men I've dated.

"The way I look at it," I say, "is that you were being virtuous in trying to help Trevor. You just got tangled in a web you didn't expect. I admire you for trying to continue your relationship with Trevor because you care about him."

Peter's eyes are sad, but I can tell by his face that he likes what I said.

"Thank you," he says in a soft voice, looking straight at me. "That was helpful."

I don't say any more. I've probably already said too much.

"I guess it's time for bed," I say, remembering he's engaged.

"I might finally get some sleep tonight," he says, "since I now have some ideas on how to resolve some of this internal conflict I've been dealing with. I really appreciate all you said, Darby."

"Goodnight," I say and walk upstairs, thinking about how many years I've wasted with failure and subsequent regret. *Time to draw a line in the sand and move on,* I tell myself. I am so much better at giving advice than taking it.

Lesson 9

The Premiere Importance of Relationships

Sunday, September 2 (the day before Labor Day)

Waking up, I realize I truly feel better without having had wine for a few days. It's also true that every morning I'm extremely glad I abstained the night before. I must remember that.

However, I still feel the usual crumminess of everything filling my head space, like an over-inflated balloon. I mean, my regret and failure with men is more than anyone could possibly... I hear it! *The Parade!* That Parade must have some severely deep grooves. What Room should I Move Into? Okay, I'll think about what I'm going to wear to church. That's simple enough. It seems that almost any Room will do.

While I'm getting ready for church, Peter texts me and asks if I want to work a couple hours on the house this afternoon. Usually I wouldn't be able to since I would need to shop and cook for Maggie's guests. But since it's Labor Day weekend, Maggie's guests are not arriving until tomorrow.

I text back that I would like to. "I've got to run to my old apartment to get my mail and a box of books, but I can meet you after that."

He texts, "Let's meet at Aunt Maggie's at 1:00. I'll pick up some lunch for us, and we can eat at the Peabody house, okay?"

"Yes, thanks," I text back. Again, a tinge of guilt crosses my mind that Peter and I are going to eat together alone, but I easily dismiss it as I remind myself that I'm his employee.

After the church service, I stop by my apartment to get my mail. Mostly bills, bills, and more bills. Then I retrieve a box of favorite books I had previously packed. The box is heavy, and I have trouble getting it down the stairs to put it in my trunk.

When I get to Maggie's, I stumble in the back door, carrying the heavy box.

"Oh, goodness," Maggie says, when she sees me. "Let's put that box in the laundry room, and we'll let Peter carry it up to your room later."

A great idea, I think.

After changing into my work clothes, I meet Peter downstairs, and we get in his truck and drive toward the house.

"What do I smell?" I ask.

"Taco salad," he says.

"I love Mexican food," I say.

"I know you do," he says with no expression but glances at me.

We drive in silence for a minute, but then Peter begins to talk.

"By the way, how have you accumulated all those great recipes you're using?"

This is so like Peter, talking to other people about their interests.

"I've been interested in international cuisine for a long time," I say. "My old boyfriend, Leland, was not a big spender, and we didn't go out much." (The dark thought that Leland has taken Bethany out multiple times begins to descend, but I Play Hot Potatoes.) "But he loved good food, so he would pay for the groceries, and I would prepare exotic meals."

"Your old boyfriend?" Peter asks. "That was recent, right?"

"Actually, we broke up only ten days ago," I say. I'm waiting for a shocked look on Peter's face, but he is as calm as ever.

"You seem to be doing okay," Peter says.

"Actually, I haven't grieved at all," I say. "The truth is that I was just coasting through life. On paper, Leland seemed like great marriage mate-rial," I add, kind of laughing, trying to make light of all this.

Peter doesn't speak, so I continue.

"I have had a little sadness," I say, "but mainly, I think it's because of the regret over wasting the last two years of my life on him. In addition, I've had to deal with some humiliation because Leland started dating a girl in my friend group two days later. So I've endured some wounded pride." I laugh again to make light of this.

"Do you think you ever loved him?" Peter asks seriously.

I don't know if I want to talk about all of this with Peter, but again, his kind eyes and direct questions have me spilling my guts. "I guess I thought I could learn to love him, but mainly—and this is embarrass-ing—I fell into a river with downstream currents and didn't even know I was being carried in it. But now that I'm out of it, I can see things clearly." I decide to leave out the part that my clock was ticking and Leland was the best I thought I was going to do, even if the fireworks were missing.

We arrive at the house and walk inside. "Let's go out on the patio and eat lunch," he suggests. Outside, we unpack our taco salads. Vegetables, free range chicken, mild salsa, lots of guacamole—it tastes divine.

The backyard is overgrown and needs attention, but I notice there are huge azalea bushes, dogwood trees, forsythia, pear trees, and red-bud trees.

"I bet this place is spectacular in the spring," I say. Peter is also look-ing over the backyard as we eat.

"I can't wait to see it," he agrees. "I want to plant some knockout rose bushes over there," he adds, as he points to an empty area. "I want this backyard to have color all spring and summer."

"I like knockout roses, too," I say, enjoying the food, the scenery, and the company. "They are my second favorite flowering shrub after lilac bushes."

"Lilac bushes?" he asks. "I've never heard anyone else say lilac bushes were their favorite shrub."

"My grandmother, Nana, used to have them in her yard when I was a child," I say. "I guess the smell is sentimental."

We eat in silence for a moment, and then Peter asks, "Have you noticed that we like a lot of the same things?" He turns to look directly at me.

"We have some common interests," I say, trying to hide my excitement at his observation.

I look back at Peter, and he doesn't smile, but he doesn't lose eye contact. I have to break his stare.

Oh, dear, I say to myself. It's true, we do like many of the same things. And it doesn't seem like he and Cassie do at all. Why is he marrying that Tyrannosaurus Rex?

I try to get my mind off Peter's perfection, but I like everything about him. I like the way he's self-controlled with money and yet generous. I like the way he treats his Aunt Maggie with affection and respect. I like the way his work ethic is focused and consistent, though not manic. I like his helpfulness with mundane tasks, his wit with his stoic face, his curly dark hair, his penetrating blue eyes, his strong forearms. The list could go on.

"Finding you to help me with this house was a game changer for me," he says, still looking at me. "I don't feel like I usually do when I'm working on a house; that is, that I'm alone, floating in an ocean."

Then I remember once again why Peter is so nice to me. I'm relieving him of stress. Sadness approaches, but I brush it away. I mean, what was I expecting? He's engaged! I'm so stupid sometimes that I read people completely wrong.

"It's nice to have another opinion," I say, hiding my sudden sadness that Peter's kindness is motivated by what I bring as an employee.

"Not only do I like your opinions," he continues, "but I enjoy working together. We get along great. Of course, you think I'm funny, and that helps," he adds.

"You are funny," I say, thinking about how relaxed and happy I am when I'm with Peter.

"Not everyone thinks I'm funny," he says, finishing his salad.

"Sure, they do," I say. "Does Cassie think you're funny?"

He looks at me with a furrowed brow. "No, not at all. Our humor is very different."

I want to say I can't believe you're marrying someone who doesn't appreciate your humor, but as usual, I don't.

"Cassie and I are pretty different in most ways," he says. I can't read what he is saying with this. He doesn't seem upset by it.

Again, I am so puzzled by Peter. He seems so bright about life in general, but then, he's marrying this girl who doesn't appreciate him and is vastly different from him. I don't get it. I just don't get it. I know she's beautiful, and men sometimes are charmed by high-brow, bratty women. I'd like to ask a follow-up question, but it seems inappropriate, so I let it go. Instead, I retreat to something superficial.

"These trees provide a lot of nice shade in the backyard," I say.

Looking up at the trees, Peter says, "Yes, I'm really falling in love with this place."

And I think to myself, *I've got to stop myself from falling in love with you.*

Finishing our lunch, we set to work and work solidly for nearly five hours.

It's almost 7:00, clearly time to call it a day. We lock up and head to the truck. Getting in the truck, Peter asks, "Are you this delightful all the time? You seem to always be in a good mood, and honestly, you do way more than your share of the work."

That's really funny since I struggle terribly with my moods. But it is true that I don't struggle much when I'm with Peter.

"You're always in a good mood, too, and you do more than your share," I say, trying to deflect the praise.

He almost smiles but instead gulps down some water. I look closely at his strong arms, his sweaty skin, and his dirty clothes from the day's work. I feel the undertow of my attraction for him, so I get hold of my mind.

Backing out of the driveway, he adds, "And Darby, I think maybe you are your *prettiest* when your hair is all scrunched up on top of your head and you're a little overheated, like now." He glances at me to read my expression before continuing to back out.

There he goes again, saying all these inappropriate—but wonderful—things to me. I can't help but smile a little.

"Especially when you smile," he adds. "Your whole face lights up when you smile."

These conversations make me feel so conflicted. I mean, they thrill me, yet I know something is very wrong. I think about how to tell him this is inappropriate, but I can't think of what to say. His text message sounds, and he says, "It's Maggie."

He hands me his phone so I can read the text out loud. "Cassie said you are picking her up at 8 p.m. at the airport. Do you and Darby have time to swing by here first to eat?"

Peter uses his dictation tool to text back, "On the way. Thanks, Aunt Maggie." Arriving at Maggie's, we head to the kitchen where Maggie has sautéed some hamburgers and baked some sweet potato fries. Eating quickly, Peter leaves to pick up Cassie.

Maggie and I chat about the upcoming week's menus, and then we do the dishes together. Just as the last dish is being put away, Cassie, followed by Peter, walks in the back door. It's clear she's annoyed. Maggie warmly greets her, but she abruptly turns to Peter. "I don't understand why you won't wear tails."

"Cassie, let's finish talking about this in my apartment," he says, and they both leave to go to his apartment.

Confused, I ask Maggie, "What is she talking about? He won't wear tails?"

"Tuxedo tails. You know, the wedding suits that look like penguins," she says.

We both laugh since Peter's personality is opposite of wearing a tuxedo like that. I start to say something, but I can hear Cassie's raised voice. She is extremely upset.

"Dear me," Maggie says, as she continues to bustle around the kitchen.

In a few minutes, Peter walks through the door alone as though nothing significant has happened. "I'm still starved. Is there anything left to eat?"

"Where's Cassie?" Maggie asks.

"She left," he said. "She said she had wedding things to do, but I think she's just mad I don't want to wear those lame tails."

Maggie turns around and raises her eyebrows at me, and I raise mine back, indicating that we understand that Cassie is one tough cookie.

It's after 9:00 p.m., so I head upstairs to my room, leaving Maggie and Peter to discuss tails.

Getting in bed to read, I'm just getting comfortable when the Genie appears.

"Hello, Young Darby." His hair is damp, and he is dressed in unusual clothes tonight, like he's been boating or swimming. "I just competed in the Annual Ancient Egyptian Regatta across the Nile River, and I won second prize. Are you ready for our lesson on relationships?"[75]

This is getting ridiculous, but I sit up in bed and get ready to take notes in my Quartz Journal.

"What's interesting to know about the subject of relationships," he begins, "is that the rules to grow great relationships are the same as they've been for 6,000 years. There are no new tricks or methods. Certain behaviors produce respectful and caring relationships, and certain behaviors repel relationships."

I don't argue, but surely we've learned something new about relationships in the last 6,000 years.

"Artificial intelligence and technology will never change the effort needed to produce great relationships," he says. "And since good relationships are the most important component of happiness, I bid you to heed the content of tonight's lesson."

---

75. Note to reader: In *Wife School* as well as *Husband School*, I wrote extensively about the specific details of drawing the human heart with admiration, appreciation, acceptance, and so on. Therefore, only an overview of the subject of relationships is presented here. Please see those books for specific details on how to grow meaningful relationships with others.

Considering my poor track record with relationships, I also bid myself to heed the content.

"Humans can live in a great setting, do work they love, be beautiful, be brilliant, and have lots of money and free time, but they can still be miserable if they don't have great relationships," he says. "Relationships are not some mystical concept that is impossible to understand. The skills and knowledge required to cultivate great relationships have been discovered and documented. Philosophers and theologians have understood the basics of great relationships for centuries."

Then you would think everyone would already know this.

"Tonight I will teach you seven principles that will enable you to catapult the intimacy and satisfaction in your relationships," he says.

Another exaggeration, but I'm getting used to them.

"Principle number one is non-negotiable in having great relationships, and it is that you must be a person others can *trust*," the Genie says. "You can do everything else right, but if you lie, are deceitful, or don't keep your promises, others will not have genuine, positive feelings toward you. It's as simple as that. No one is smart enough to break this rule and get by with it indefinitely. Eventually, those without integrity in a relationship will be found out, and others will pull away emotionally. Therefore, be trustworthy to the highest degree."

I'm not one to outright lie, but I admit I can sometimes be a little manipulative. I vow right now to do better.

"The second principle to understand about relationships is that they always—always—have a sowing and reaping component," he says. "A good analogy to explain this concept is the care of a garden. When given sunlight, water, nutrient-dense soil, frequent weeding, and protection from predators, lush gardens predictably grow. But when gardens are thirsty for water, have poor soil, or are overrun with disease and predators, the result is predictably barren gardens. Relationships are like gardens. Certain situations always produce lush gardens, and certain situations always produce barren gardens. Let's discuss what grows and what stunts relationships."

I'm all ears.

"Examples of qualities and actions that grow relationships are giving admiration, attention, appreciation, and acceptance. In addition, performing acts of service, giving gifts, being trustworthy, and being responsible grow relationships. Agree wholeheartedly but disagree softly. Be affirming, loyal, and in a good mood. Offer others compassion, kindness, and patience as well as tenderness, warmth, and mercy. Do more than your share. All these qualities and actions draw one human heart to another."

Gulp. I can't be Mother Teresa.

"Likewise, there are qualities and actions that repel others such as dishonesty, criticism, and negativity. Giving too much advice and insisting on being right drives others away. People avoid those who are irresponsible, undependable, lazy, complaining, or selfish."

Gulp. Another convicting list.

"Human relationships cannot withstand continual negativity or they wither and die," he says.

My mother comes to mind.

"The third principle one must understand to grow meaningful relationships is that people have a longing to be known and understood. They want you to know how they feel, what they want, and the content of their dreams and calling. They want you to discern what is important to them."

Well, duh. I'd like that, too.

"Therefore, it is imperative that you learn and develop the skills of Asking World-Class Questions and Giving World-Class Listening," he says.

Oh, no. What's this?

"Asking World-Class Questions allows other people to talk about what they are interested in. You encourage others to keep talking by maintaining eye contact and continuing to ask them questions such as 'What happened next?' and 'Tell me more.' People love to talk about their ideas, opinions, and activities, but only to others who are interested."

I'm genuinely interested in people, so I might actually be good at this one thing.

"Giving World-Class Listening is a rare skill, but it draws the human heart like the moon draws the tides."

People have told me I'm a good listener. *Finally,* I'm good at something.

"Intentionally seek to understand another," he says. "Determine to listen twice as much as you talk. This is life-altering to many."

Well, I do tend to talk a lot, so I could work on this.

"The fourth principle we will discuss tonight to skyrocket the depth and satisfaction of your relationships is to make a decision to *initiate for the other person's benefit.* That is, decide to help those in your inner circle get what they want. *Sacrifice to help them with their happiness and goals.* Have a mindset that you give more than you take."

What a nice world it would be if everyone did this.

"Unfortunately, instead of intentionally initiating for another's benefit," he continues, "many people let their relationships coast. But just like gardens, relationships need continual attention and care."

I could have used better attention and care when I was growing up and—Hot Potatoes! There I go, blaming my mom again.

"Therefore, study how to improve another's welfare," he says. "Be a person who helps other people's lives get better by helping them with their goals and happiness. *Love is a decision to act in the best interest of another.*"

I love that. I want to be a person like that. I write that sentence in my Quartz Journal and put stars around it.

"The fifth principle to grow and deepen relationships is to know how to react when another person's *weakness set* disappoints," he says. "All people are half strengths and half weaknesses. That means everyone in your inner circle will have a weakness set (such as lack of attention, lack of dependability, and more). You must have a system to know how to think about and deal with another's weakness set instead of being massively disappointed."

A system to deal with others' weakness sets? Instead of being massively disappointed? This I've got to hear.

"The secret is, again, to forego and overlook," he says. "I taught you how to not be offended in Lesson 7. If you remember, I said foregoing and overlooking are similar to being like smoke and letting the other person's offense pass through you. This is in contrast to being a brick wall and having the offense abruptly land. Overlook others' weaknesses."

I still have to figure this out with my mom and Bailey.

"Of course, sometimes others will ignore you, keep you waiting, treat you rudely, show others preference, interrupt you, criticize you, complain about you, be negative, or be annoying. But you as a human can choose how to interpret all those events. You can interpret them as disappointing and 'awfulize' their actions, or you can forego and overlook.[76] You can learn to *reconstrue thoughts that seem negative*. Remember, things are only a certain way if you construe them to be."

I've already forgotten most of this material. This course is going too fast.

"So refuse to be offended, and instead, continue to focus on how *you* love and give," he says.

This is pretty lofty teaching. I wonder what percentage of the population lives by these rules—1 percent?

"Remember the lesson on forgiving?" he asks. "To forgive another, you take their box of grievances and turn the box upside down, emptying its contents. You empty their accounts. Bitterness makes your soul tiny, warped, mangled, and shriveled. Nothing is worse for the human heart than bitterness. Refuse to keep any bitterness toward anyone. Forgive extravagantly. The only free person is the person who can forgive."

I've got to find the strength somewhere to forgive my mom.[77]

"The sixth major principle that I want to discuss today is to drop the expectation that others will love and give to you in the manner you

---

76. Of course, there are times when you must lovingly confront others. But the current culture suggests we need to repeatedly stand up for our rights and confront every possible offense. How opposite this is to what Proverbs 19:11 (NIV) says, that "it is to one's glory to overlook an offense."

77. In *Happy School Advanced*, we extensively study the subject of forgiveness.

prefer. Instead, shift from focusing on who doesn't love and give to you enough to focusing on how *you* love and give to others. Yes, humans naturally focus on how they aren't treated right by others, aren't respected enough, honored enough, or given enough attention and praise. Get rid of these expectations that others will treat you special and that they will be grateful and appreciative. This thinking causes self-pity."

Okay, when I'm offended, I've got to focus on how I love and give, not on how I'm *not* being loved or given to. This will take some Herculean effort.

"The seventh principle to enhance and deepen your relationships is to develop humility," he says. "This is probably the hardest task of all. Take the blame, give the credit. Cheerfully take correction and constructive criticism. Be smoke, and try to learn from others' accusations. (Usually there is a hair of truth in most criticism.) Humans hate to admit they are wrong, but you should be quick to say, 'I was wrong. Will you please forgive me?'"

"Genie, I have a couple questions," I say. "These principles may work with normal people, but what about toxic people like my mother?"

"If possible, when people are repeatedly difficult and toxic and you have repeatedly tried and failed to resolve the conflict (for example, with your ex-boss, Jana), it is best to remove yourself from those environments, if possible.[78] But of course, the guidelines are different for parents and children."[79]

I was afraid of that.

"Let's discuss a few principles to know in dealing with difficult family members," he begins. "Of course, I am assuming you have repeatedly tried to resolve conflict with these family members but have failed."

Tried and tried. Failed and failed.

---

78. Christians are instructed to return good for evil and return a blessing for insult, but this does not mean you have to always continue to be in close relationships with toxic people. Relationships are discussed in much more detail in *Happy School Advanced*.

79. Christians are called to honor their parents, but this doesn't mean adult children still have to obey. Honoring toxic parents will be discussed in *Happy School Advanced*.

"Here is a helpful principle for setting boundaries with difficult relatives," he says.

Answer their calls only on holidays?

"The instruction is to go the proverbial 'first mile,'" he says. "Then, as instructed in the Creator's Word, go the second mile with your toxic relative. Going the second mile means doing more than what is expected."

Bummer. Super bummer.

"But here's the happy part," he says. "You do not have to go the *third mile*. That's where you set boundaries. This is the principle that protects you from getting sucked into a toxic person's negative world. You go the first and second miles and then draw a line in the sand. You don't have to do more. You won't believe *how going the second mile* will calm down most toxic people. This strategy's power is similar to the way a gentle answer turns away wrath."[80]

I like this. I really do. I know I can never completely withdraw from my mother (although I am certainly often tempted), but this gives me a template. I can be in a relationship with her and give her the "second mile" (give more than I think I should), but then I can stop. I can draw a line and withdraw. I like having a principle so I know I won't be swallowed up by her dark side.

"I want to express again that you have much control over your emotions in dealing with difficult people," he says, "by Moving into Another Room in Your Brain as well as giving external situations more positive interpretations."

The same advice, over and over again.

"In addition," he continues, "I want you to know that hard people are sometimes a gift in disguise because they enable you to clearly see what you *don't* want to become. Just because you grew up with a critical and negative parent or guardian does not mean you are doomed to duplicate those thinking patterns. Remember, the brain is plastic and can change. You are now an adult and can choose to renew and reprogram your mind. You can break a previously unhealthy, generational cycle."

---

80. Proverbs 15:1

That's fabulous news. I have been afraid I was destined to become my mother.

"To summarize, no one is coming on a white horse to help you form deep, meaningful relationships," he says. "And since relationships are about 70 percent of your happiness, you must take responsibility to initiate and form them yourself.[81] Remember, how you care for others is a measure of your true greatness."[82]

This is opposite to how I was brought up. I was taught that position, power, money, looks, and control were the measure of greatness.

"Before I leave, I want you to think about whether you have offended or harmed anyone," he says. "And if you have, you need to go to them, admit you were wrong, and ask their forgiveness. In many circles, this is called Making Amends, and it is absolutely crucial that you do so in order to get emotional freedom. Learn to apologize quickly when you err. Having a clear conscience toward others not only restores relationships but is vital to having a happy heart."

I'll have to process this later about my mother and Bailey. Usually, I focus only on how they offend me, never on how I might offend them.

He twirls into a tornado of air and vanishes. I fall asleep wondering how I'm going to implement half of what the Genie said on relationships. But if relationships are 70 percent of my happiness, it is worth my time to heed this advice.

Monday morning, September 3, Labor Day

I put on my workout clothes, add a tiny bit of mascara, blush, and lipstick, and head downstairs. Maggie is in the kitchen by herself in her usual, upbeat mood.

---

81. Be sure to focus on how *you* love and give to others, not on how others don't love and give *to you*, as that is a WMD and a Room to Stay Out Of.
82. "The greatest among you will be your servant" (Matthew 23:11 NIV).

I begin to scramble some eggs as Maggie drinks her coffee. I sit down on a bar stool beside her at the breakfast bar, and she begins. "It's been so great to reconnect with you again, Darby. I always had such affection for you when you were in college."

"I'm glad we've reconnected again, too," I say.

"How is your mother doing?" she asks.

I remember one afternoon more than ten years ago when I met with Maggie and sobbed in her kitchen as I told her about my parents' divorce. I fill Maggie in on the last ten years—my father making it big financially, his death, my mother trying to get the inheritance Daddy left me, and now my mother trying to persuade me to put Nana in a nursing home. Telling Maggie my problems is just as easy now as it was ten years ago.

"How sweet you are to Nana," she says. "I'm sure if she were able to thank you, she would."

That comment opens up some underground waterworks in me, and I fight hard to keep back the tears.

I tell Maggie about one of my mother's recent hysterics when she blamed me for her failed romance. Maggie just shakes her head. "I'm so sorry," she says.

Of course I don't bring up the Genie, but I do say that I don't think I'm the same person I used to be. I explain to Maggie how I'm learning to *not* focus on What's Missing and Disappointing (the WMDs) but on positive thoughts such as accomplishing goals and giving away my gifts.

Maggie seems a little startled. "Many fifty- and sixty-year-olds don't understand these principles," she says, "and you are learning this in your early thirties. Those secrets are certainly excellent for mental health. I'm proud of you, Darby."

"Heaven knows I needed to change my thinking patterns," I say. Maggie's kindness makes me feel such affection for her.

Abruptly, the back door swings open, and Cassie walks in. As usual, she ignores the hired help. "Aunt Maggie, I just remembered about thirty more people I need to invite."

This might be the rudest person I've ever met.

Even though cool and collected, Maggie is shaken by her tone. "Why, Cassie, where will we put everyone? It was going to be tight before. I'm just not sure this house can support a party that large."

Peter walks in now. Apparently he knows the topic. "Aunt Maggie is being very generous to throw the reception, Cassie, so can't you pare back the invitation list?"

"Peter! I'm the bride," she snarls, "and these are things brides get to decide."

The tension in the room is thick. Maggie looks at Cassie and softly says, "Well, if we're crowded, then we will just be crowded. It'll be a little cooler by then, and maybe we could put some tables and chairs out on the patio so people can mosey out there."

"That's a good idea, Aunt Maggie," Cassie says, cooling down. "We can put tables and chairs on the patio." And with that, she and Peter go outside. He walks her to her car before she leaves.

Peter returns and says to Aunt Maggie, "You didn't have to do that. If you don't want that many people here, it's your house, so you should get to decide."

"This seems so important to Cassie, and I want to be as accommodating as I possibly can," Maggie says in her reasonable voice. "If we're a little crowded, it doesn't matter. What matters is that we try not to ruffle the bride's feathers."

"It drives me crazy," Peter says, shaking his head.

"Lots of girls get emotional and upset over wedding things," Maggie says in a soft voice, as if she's discussing a lovely summer day. "We will do the best we can to make her happy. Cassie is not usually unreasonable."

"She certainly can be," he says, and he is not laughing when he says that.

Since I need more ingredients to make the salad tonight, I have an excuse to run to the store. These Cassie moments make me so uncomfortable.

At the grocery store, I see Bailey across the produce aisles. I wave, but she quickly turns away like she didn't recognize me. That's weird,

I tell myself. Quickly I follow her as she pushes her basket around the corner. When I round the corner, I see that she has stopped and already taken one earring out. She is trying to remove the other one—the other diamond stud earring!

"Bailey!" I say, shocked, wanting an explanation. "Are those Nana's diamond studs?"

The blood drains from Bailey's face. Both of us simply stare at each other.

"I didn't think it was fair that Nana is leaving you more inheritance than me, so I just thought it was fine if I went and got these earrings."

I can't even talk. I'm so outraged. I just look at her in disbelief.

"It's not really stealing," she says. "Nana had no business giving you more inheritance than me. I'm just evening the score."

"Bailey, Nana decides who gets what, not us," I say. "You are supposed to get the diamond brooch, but I am supposed to get those earrings. It's all written out in her will."

"How was I supposed to know that since only *you* get to see 'The Secret Will'?" she says. "Well, here, you can have them." She takes one diamond stud out of her purse and the other one out of her ear. "Still, it's not right that you're getting more inheritance."

I'm still shell-shocked that Bailey would take jewelry from Nana's safe. I knew Bailey was self-absorbed, but stealing crosses a new line.

After checking out, I drive home in a daze. Stealing? How am I supposed to forgive her for that? I understand that she feels she should get an equal portion of the inheritance, but Nana didn't want to give her 50 percent. I'm furious, just furious. Bailey has virtually ignored Nana her whole life, but now she just takes what she wants from Nana's safe—and lies about it!

Lesson 10

The Importance of a
Morning Happiness Routine (MHR)

Still Monday, September 3, Labor Day

By the time I get to Maggie's, I feel like a zombie. Knowing I've got to start cooking, I command myself to think about my work. But my mind keeps going back to Bailey. My own sister, stealing. It's heartbreaking.

Some of Maggie's guests are coming in on Tuesday, so it's a small crowd for dinner tonight. My energy is down, so it's just as well.

Everyone seemed to enjoy the meal, but I am still steamed over Bailey.

After the dishes are cleaned up, Maggie asks Peter to carry my heavy box of books up to my room. Not wanting to impose on Peter, I say, "I can do it, Maggie."

Neither Peter nor Maggie respond to me, but Peter walks straight to the pantry, picks up the box, and starts up the stairs.

"Are you collecting gold bricks?" he asks.

"No," I say, usually enjoying Peter's lightheartedness, but not tonight. "Those are just some of my favorite books." I can't get Bailey out of my mind.

He sets the box on the floor by my chaise lounge and glances at the bills strewn across my credenza. I forgot I had left them in clear view. I was always careful to hide them from Leland.

Picking them up, he asks, "MasterCard? American Express? Visa? Zara? Anthropology? Nordstrom's? What's all this?"

First I'm embarrassed, and then I'm annoyed that I've been found out. And besides, who is Peter to ask me such a personal question? It's none of his business.

But what do I care? What do I care if Peter knows I'm a complete loser with a spending problem that is eating up my inheritance? It actually would feel good to tell someone, to come out of my secret debtor's cave.

"I have a little trouble with spending," I say. I look up at his face.

"What kind of trouble?" he asks.

"Uh, I have trouble with buying stuff. I'm kind of in debt," I admit. I don't even care what he thinks. My sister steals, and my life is horrible. I can hear my Parade Marching across my Brain, and I know I need to take charge of it. But I'm so tired of fighting. I'm *exhausted* from the struggle.

Go ahead, I want to say. *Let me have it. I deserve it. Give me a verbal lashing for being such a loser.* I look at him defiantly, urging him with my expression to bring it on.

Peter's face, however, is not judgmental at all. "How do you handle that financially? I mean, how do you even pay the minimum?"

Do I tell the real truth? Why not? I'm weary and sick of everything.

"Well," I begin, not being sure I want to confess all of this, "I...uh...I have some inheritance from my dad that I'm using to pay the minimum." I've never said that out loud. I decide not to tell Peter that I thought I'd soon have an ophthalmologist paying my bills.

"Darby, you can't be perfect," he says, again with his calm and glistening eyes. "There are a lot worse things than not knowing how to perfectly control your spending. Being on a budget is actually an easy skill to learn. Would you like me to help you with that?"

Normally I would say no, but I'm so emotional since I found out about Bailey's theft that I just don't have the strength to Move into Another Room. Big tears drop down my cheek at Peter's lack of judgment and his kind offer to help.

"Why are you crying?" he asks.

"It's been a rough day," I say, and then I tell him about Bailey and the earrings.

"People can be disappointing," he says.

My mother. My sister. Leland. Bethany.

We talk a little more about the Bailey situation, and he listens carefully. When I'm finished, Peter doesn't give any advice. He just says he's sorry.

Then he changes the subject.

"Why don't you give me all these credit card bills and let me help you get a bill consolidation loan? Did you know you are paying about 25 percent interest on some of these credit cards?"

"Actually, I thought it was only 18 percent," I say, trying to lessen the sting.

He ignores my comment. "Let me have your bills, and I'll work on a plan for you."

I'd argue, but I don't have the strength.

"Do you mind if I get the e-mail and passwords you use so I can check your actual balances?" he asks.

I know I'm not supposed to share my passwords with anyone, but Peter is about as safe as a bank vault. And I do need some help. I willingly tell him. "My e-mail is DarbyMcKesney@gmail.com, and my password is GourmetCook4."

"What does the number 4 stand for?" he asks. Peter is not prying. He is simply interested in other people, as usual.

Again, what does it matter if he knows my loser secrets?

I'm embarrassed to tell him, but I do it anyway. "It's how many children I want someday." As soon as I say it, I wish I hadn't.

Peter jumps right in. "There we go again, being the same. That's how many I want."

Our eyes lock, and there's that strange connection, almost like you could feel the electricity jumping back and forth between us. I break the eye contact so I don't get burned.

Well, I can't worry about that right now. I need help with my bills. And I work for him, so it's fine if we're together and he helps me.

Even though I feel an undertow with this chemistry for Peter, I have to remember he's merely being friendly and that's he's *not* pursuing me. Maybe Peter is such a good ol' boy that he doesn't even know he's being *too* nice. Maybe he thinks this is the way to treat all women.

All I know is that Peter Needleman makes me more excited than any man I've ever met. And he's kinder than any man I've ever met and more handsome than any man I've ever met. But I can't have him, and I never will and—oh dear! Hot Potatoes! The Parade is Marching. I command myself with what little strength I have to get out of that self-pity zone.

After Peter leaves, I go into my bathroom to take off my makeup. I think about what Room to Move Into, but I don't have any strength. Instead, I just let myself cry. *Go to bed,* I tell myself. Things are always better in the morning. The idea of getting a glass of wine to dial down my emotions appears, but I'm getting pretty good at quickly slapping my brain with the reasoning and the persuasion of the proclamation of My Best Sane Higher Self. *You'll be glad in the morning that you didn't succumb to this ambush,* I always tell myself. And it's true. Every morning I'm glad I'm living an alcohol-free life.

Getting in bed, I realize how exhausted I am. I'm hugely offended by Bailey. I have gigantic self-pity that I'm single. Yes, the WMDs in life are pressing in, but I quickly dose off.

Tuesday morning, September 4, 6:30 a.m.

Waking up, I glance outside and notice the beautiful sunlight. I've had nine of the ten *Happy School* lessons, and although my knowledge of what to think has grown dramatically, I still have deep grooves of negative thinking patterns. I guess I shouldn't expect all of my emotional issues to be solved in ten days. The Genie says this is a five-year program, so I can't be upset that everything is not yet completely fixed. I do see, however, that following his advice, I could eventually become a different person.

Walking to my coffee pot, I notice a familiar mood descending, one that is not especially upset over anything in particular but just a general malaise. What's going on? Emotions come from thoughts, so I obviously must be thinking something negative. What could it be?

Before I can process what thoughts are causing my emotions, the Genie appears. "Good morning, Young Darby. Today is our final lesson, Lesson 10. It is called Establishing a Morning Happiness Routine." He hands me my Quartz Journal.

"Our final lesson?" I ask, thinking my mastery of the *Happy School* curriculum is similar to a baby who is now crawling but still needs the constant care and attention of an adult.

"Yes, the final lesson," he says. "To begin today," he says, "I want to give you an analogy for your brain in the early morning."

My brain is thick mud in the morning. Like right now, for example.

"In the 1800s, before electricity, homes were often heated in the winter by a wood-burning stove, which was frequently located in the basement. In the early morning, someone would go down into the basement and start a fire with wood inside the stove. The stove was connected to pipes that traveled all over the house to various rooms, carrying the stove's heat in them. In winter, a house was extremely cold in the mornings until someone started the fire, and then the heat of the logs from the basement stove was carried throughout the pipes to the various rooms."

I'm not sure I need a lecture about nineteenth-century heating.

"I want you to see your brain in the morning as the unheated house," he says. "You have to put logs in the basement stove and start the fire. Soon the house—your brain—will be heated up. I am going to give you five ideas (logs) you can use every morning to warm up your mind to a positive state. Some people wake up in a sunny, warm emotional state, just like some people wake up in a sunny, warm physical climate. Knowing that you wake up in a cold, emotional environment means you have to take proactive steps every morning to warm up your mind and perspective."

I hate it that I'm broken. I hate it that I have to work so hard to be happy when others naturally just are. Uh-oh. I just heard self-pity. Hot Potatoes.

"This daily routine is called a Morning Happiness Routine (MHR) and is of utmost importance to jump-start your mind to think positively and correctly. There are five aspects to a Morning Happiness Routine, and I will walk you through each of them in today's lesson."

This sounds like way too much work. I don't have time for *five* aspects—maybe one or two. He's always so overboard.

"The first aspect of the MHR is creating a Gratefulness Practice. So please write *Gratefulness* at the top of a page. On the next page, write My Genius Zone and My Current Top Life Goals. Label the third page My Enjoyment Log and What I'm Looking Forward To. The fourth page is called Penning Up the Farmyard Animals. We will save the fifth aspect for the end.[83]

That is over-the-top ridiculous, as usual. I have to complain. "Genie, this seems a little much," I say.

"Young Darby, if you had diabetes, you would check your blood sugar every morning and eat something if it's low. You'd give yourself a shot if it was high. If you had problems walking, you would attach a brace to your leg every morning. You personally have trouble with discouragement, and your very life's happiness is at stake. This twenty-minute Morning Happiness Routine is a small price to pay for giving yourself the advantage of a positive mindset first thing every morning. The benefits are astronomical."

I used to mock the Genie when he used words like *astronomical,* but now that I'm finding some freedom—not total freedom, but some—I believe that maybe these principles are, after all, life-changing.[84]

"Once you learn the MHR habit, you will not spend much time at this exercise at all," he says.

I'm to do *five* things without spending much time?

---

83. Bible reading and prayer will be discussed more in *Happy School Advanced.*
84 They are life-changing because they are all based on biblical principles.

"Let's begin with step one of your MHR, the Gratitude Practice," he says. "As soon as you gain consciousness in the morning—before you even get out of bed—begin listing things you're grateful for. This is a habit for you to do first thing every morning for the rest of your life."

Usually I wake up to my WMDs pressing in, but he's telling me to take charge of my mind and begin each day with a Gratefulness Practice. That will be a different start, for sure.

"Let's begin your list of items for which you're grateful. I will help you get the first ten entries down," he says. "This list will soon grow to twenty, and then thirty, and so on."

I sit quietly while he stares at me. "Uh, well, I guess I'm grateful for…uh, my eyes and that I can see."

"Continue," he says without emotion.

"I am grateful that I can walk and that I can breathe clean air," I say. He waits while I continue to write.

"I am grateful for, uh, clean water and healthy food," I say, starting to get on a roll, "and indoor plumbing and an emergency room at a nearby hospital, if I need one."

He still doesn't say anything. I continue to write, "Electricity, freedom in America…okay, that's ten things. I guess there's quite a bit to be grateful for," I admit.

"Exactly, but you haven't been trained to *hunt* for it," he says. "We must rewire your brain so you repeatedly focus on thinking about *all the good* and *all the benefits* that you *do* have in your life (and, of course, quarantine your thinking about the unpleasant subjects to the three times we continually review). Developing a gratefulness practice has invaluable healing in it."

Quickly, I add to the list that I'm grateful for getting a new job (getting away from Toxic Jana, that I've conquered my weight problem,[85] and that I have a good mind).

---

85. *Skinny School* will teach you how to *think* about food so you no longer want Trash Food. After reading *Skinny School*, you can develop further mastery in knowing how to think correctly about food by reading the free, online lessons, *Skinny School Advanced*, available at JulieNGordon.com.

"Now for the second of the five MHR activities," he says. "Rewrite your Genius Zone on this page and also your Current Top Life Goals. We discussed this in Lesson 5, so just rewrite them here.[86] The natural mind easily forgets its mission and vision and therefore needs to be reminded daily."

That one was easy. "What's next?" I ask.

"The third list is called My Enjoyment Log and What I'm Looking Forward To. It is *your* responsibility to make time to enjoy your life, not anyone else's. Often people focus on their WMDs to such an extent that they don't take responsibility for adding activities that add joy to their life."

"I do love cooking and design, and I am finally doing work in those areas," I say. Until recently, I had few activities I liked in my life besides online shopping and my wine habit.[87]

"These first three lists are all 'logs in the stove' that warm up your mind with positive thought," he says.

I guess I could try this since mornings are usually especially discouraging.

"The fourth list in your MHR is called Penning Up the Farmyard Animals," he says.[88] "Imagine that you are a farmer, and every night while you sleep, someone unlocks the gates to all the farmyard animals' pens. In the morning, they are wildly running throughout the farm. Therefore, every morning the farmer has to round them up and get them back in the pen. The farmyard animals are your WMDs that run amok in your mind every morning. Therefore, write down each morning all the problems pressing you. What you will soon see is that you have the same negative

---

86. In the free online lessons *Happy School Advanced,* there will be articles to help you work through each of these items in your Quartz Journal. In addition, as I frequently say, meeting with a couple like-minded friends and doing the online lessons together greatly increase effectiveness. Go to JulieNGordon.com, and click on the tab that says Lessons.

87. Self-discipline was discussed in Lesson 4.

88. For a Christian, this might also include a time of confession. Resentment, unkind feelings, bitterness, and more must be forsaken. I cover this carefully in the free online lessons in *Happy School Advanced.*

thoughts and problems every morning. If you problem-solve and work on your problems (in one of the three times allowed), you will realize that you are making progress. For example, a week ago you hated your work, and now you are doing two jobs you enjoy."

I'm getting used to him calling everything by a lame name. And it doesn't annoy me anymore.

"Penning up the Farmyard Animals is incredibly beneficial because you get them out of your mind and onto paper where you can deal with them later," he says. "Quarantining problems by putting them in boxes with tops until a later time when you can problem-solve is one of the most valuable skills you've learned in *Happy School*."

Learning it and doing it are two different ducks.

"The fifth and last MHR activity is to have inspirational reading[89] ready in the morning so you can bathe your mind with hopeful and truthful thoughts. This may be the most important 'log' of all."

I think giving up my wine habit will help me get up earlier, which I'll need since the Genie is laying this new routine on my back.

"I will offer one more 'log' to add to your stove, Young Darby. It is an optional log but one I highly recommend. The log is to engage in morning outdoor exercise. The combination of fresh air, an increased heart rate, and sunlight (even if it's cloudy) seems to greatly improve one's mood."

Although I subconsciously already know this, it's good to hear it so I will work harder to get outside in the early morning.

"I am not saying it is easy to begin, develop, and continue a Morning Happiness Routine," he says, "but I am saying that it is *invaluable* to increasing your emotional well-being."

"Genie, I was hoping that after I had been in *Happy School* this long, I would wake up with a happy heart and tap dance throughout the day."

---

89. Many morning devotionals exist, and they are excellent sources to help bathe your mind with truth and hope. For example, I love Charles Spurgeon's devotional *Beside Still Waters*, as well as Oswald Chambers' *My Utmost for His Highest*. I also highly recommend that you read the Bible every morning and pray.

"Your prior brain grooves are deep," he says, "and will take a few years to rebuild. But having a Morning Happiness Routine is another great tool in your arsenal for building new, life-changing neural pathways. I will return one more time to bid you farewell, Young Darby," and he swirls into an invisible funnel of air.

Actually, I like that last lesson, stoking a fire in my brain by adding certain "logs." I see how this could be helpful, especially over time.

Walking into my bathroom, I brush my teeth and get ready for the day. Suddenly, out of nowhere, a new idea for Peter's house appears to me, and I love it. But before I can completely refine the idea in my mind, Peter calls. We're supposed to meet to work on his house in an hour.

"Cassie is getting stressed out about the musicians in the wedding, and Aunt Maggie thinks I should help her with it," he says. I hear the frustration in his voice. "Honestly, I don't see why she can't take care of it herself."

Again, I ponder the strangeness of their relationship.

"Okay," I say. "I'll meet you at the house later, but can I run an idea past you first?"

"Go ahead," he says.

"I haven't completely figured this out, but I think there are enough square feet in the master bedroom upstairs to pull back the wall a little bit and make an enclosed, screened-in balcony porch that would be a private sitting area off the master bedroom."

There's a silence, and I think he must hate the idea. Then he says, "I was wondering how to make a screened-in porch area on the patio downstairs but how much more I would enjoy it off the master bedroom, This may be your best idea yet."

"I love screened-in porches," I say. The thought of Peter and rude Cassie enjoying the beautiful Memphis evenings on that balcony porch brings me down for a moment, but I know to invoke Hot Potatoes immediately.

He's quiet for a second, and so am I. "There we go again," he says, and we both know he's talking about how we enjoy the same things.

I laugh, "Yes, there we go." The longing reappears, but I again successfully Hot Potato it out one more time.

Driving over to the house, I notice that the neighborhood is extremely quiet and peaceful. The huge trees remind me of a stability that I wish I had.

At the house, I walk outside on the patio and gaze at the hot pink crepe myrtles in full bloom. September is when their color is the richest. The familiar distant ache and longing reappear, and I know it is about Peter. I never felt that way about Leland. It's as if I didn't even know before now that men like Peter existed. I mean, I've dated countless men, and this ache is something I've never had before. I know I must fight it, but sometimes I'm tired of fighting. I wonder if it's wise to continue to work with him. Maybe I should quit. Being together all the time just fuels my longings.

Before getting started on the measurements for the balcony porch, I check my e-mail. What's this? I've got several e-mails from Zara, Master-Card, and others. Clicking on each one, they similarly say, "Thank you for your payment."

I call Peter back, and he answers with, "Great timing. I just left Cassie, and she's calmed down."

Ignoring his comment, I say, "I'm getting e-mails from my credit card companies. Someone paid off all of my credit cards."

"Darby, I want you to listen to me before you get worked up, okay?" He knows what I'm implying. "If I had hired an interior designer or an architect to do the work that you've done in the last ten days, I would have paid way more money than this. We agreed that I would pay you after we finished the house, but I decided to go ahead and give you a bonus now. So I am paying you what your work has been worth so far, and that's equal to paying off your credit cards."

"Peter, I owed $5,000!"

"And your help with the house has been worth $10,000, so I still think I owe you another $5,000," he says.

"I can't let you do this," I argue.

"It's business, Darby. Of course, you can. But I do hope you'll let me help you get on a budget and help you invest your father's inheritance. And what about your car? You're paying a steep note on that car, right?"

I don't answer.

"I thought so," he says. "You might need to sell that fine machine and get something more economical."

After the Genie's talk on self-discipline and stopping bad habits, I know Peter's right, but I do love my Lexus. It's so sleek and upscale.

"I'm on my way to the house. See you at 11:00," he says, and we hang up.

After measuring and designing the balcony screened-in porch, I realize it's going to work better than I had hoped.

While waiting for Peter to arrive, I think about how he spellbinds me. Not that he intentionally does, but he definitely does. I need to move on with my life, and it's very hard when I'm working for him every day and am repeatedly bewitched by his charms. I decide to tell him that I'm going to quit. I've completed the design of the house, so now is a good stopping point. He's paid me by paying off my credit cards, so this is a doubly good time to quit.

Peter arrives and has something in his hands, but I can't see what it is because his back is to me. After he hears me walk in behind him, he turns around. In his hands is a lilac bush.

"That's a lilac bush," I say.

"Is it?" he asks with a straight face. "I have just the place to plant it."

"Why did you buy that?" I ask.

He looks directly at me. "Because you said it was your favorite flowering shrub."

This has got to stop. Maybe he's too dense to know what he's doing. I'm stunned by his gesture, but of course, I'm charmed.

I decide to go ahead and tell him I'm quitting. "Thank you for paying off those credit cards—I really do appreciate it—but that's way too generous of you to pay me $5,000 for my work."

"No it's not," he counters. "It was good work for a good price." His eyes are warm yet piercing with intelligence and energy.

"Well, uh, I, uh, I wanted to tell you that, uh, I'm not going to be able to work for you anymore," I stammer.

"What's the matter, Darby?" he asks, stopping suddenly and turning toward me.

"It's just that, well, I've designed your house like I said I would—and by the way, here are the measurements for the screened-in balcony porch—but now, I'm, well, I'm through," I say.

"Could you please tell me what is really going on?" he asks. He is obviously and understandably puzzled.

I refuse to tell him. I can't tell him. There's nothing good that could come from it.

"I'm going to make detailed lists of everything that still needs to be done," I say, "but I'm through. You've paid me—although too much—so this is a good place for me to bow out."

"Something happened. Tell me what happened." His eyes don't move.

"It's a decision I've made," I say. "I've got some more work I need to do for Maggie's dinner tonight so I'll see you at dinner." I don't really have much more work, but I don't want him to badger me anymore about why I'm quitting.

"I don't understand," he says, and I can tell by his eyes that he is hurt.

"It's for the best," I say and head for my car to drive away.

The Genie Departs

Still Tuesday, September 3, 8:00 p.m.

I served dinner as usual, but Peter was very quiet. Even Maggie noticed and asked him if everything was okay. He walked into the kitchen carrying some of the dirty dinner plates.

"I think you owe me an explanation," he says.

I start to answer, but there is a knock at the door.

Peter walks to the door, and I hear a familiar voice. "Is Darby McKesney here?"

Now my heart starts to race. Peter comes back to the kitchen, followed by Leland who still has on his scrubs and long, white physician's coat.

"Leland!" I say, surprised out of my mind.

"Hi, Darby," he says with a humble, downcast face. Leland has always seemed so handsome in the past, but tonight, he looks weak. Nothing about him is desirable.

I introduce Peter and Maggie to Leland, and Peter excuses himself to go to his in-law suite.

"Can we go somewhere and talk?" he asks.

"Well, I have to finish my work here," I say.

"Nonsense," Maggie says. "I'm happy to finish. Go ahead, Darby. I'll see you in the morning."

I have no idea what this is about, and I'm very uncomfortable.

"Let's go to Starbucks," he says.

"Leland, is it okay if we just sit in your car and talk a second?" I want him to state his business and be gone.

He agrees, and we walk outside to sit in his car. The car smells familiar, a mixture of a new car mingled with the Irish Spring soap he uses. He looks at me, and I can tell he's a little nervous.

"Darby," he says, turning toward me as much as he can. "I made a terrible mistake." He pauses, gathering his thoughts.

I wait to hear more.

"I think it might be the worst mistake of my life. I let the girl of my dreams get away."

"What are you talking about, Leland? You said you had decided you weren't going to marry me."

"My mother, as you know, has quite an influence on me. But I've been sick without you."

"Bethany's posts on Facebook didn't look like you were sick."

"A huge mistake," he says. "I fell into going out with her because she was available, and she kept suggesting things. But I looked at her one night and realized how much I miss you, your wit, your intelligence..."

"My cooking?" I ask.

For the first time, he smiles. "Yes, I definitely miss your cooking."

He continues. "I called my mom. I told her I love you and that I have let her influence me in a way I shouldn't have."

I wait again.

"She said my happiness was the most important thing and that she could learn to overlook the things that upset her about you. She is going to accept you, Darby."

Well, how about that? The Wicked Witch of the West is going to learn to accept me. Isn't that dandy?

I decide not to comment and instead ask, "How did you find me?"

"I texted Ellie, and she told me," he says.

Right. It's hard to hide these days.

"This is not how I pictured things, but," Leland stops talking and pulls a little black velvet box out of his coat pocket. "Darby, will you please marry me?" He opens the box, and inside is a beautiful, sparkly (large!) diamond ring.

I remember all the times I dreamed of this moment, for Leland to pull out a little black velvet box. And now I'm repulsed at his arrogance, thinking he can humiliate me with The Girls, make a quick about-face, and find me still there panting like a puppy. Just disgusting.

I look at Leland, and he is smiling, hopeful, and happy.

"Leland, a lot has happened in the last two weeks," I begin. "And as much as I respect several things about you, I have realized I am not in love with you. I was in love with being your wife at one point, but I am not really in love *with you*." There's no need to tell him I was in love with his position and his paycheck. That makes me sound shallow.

"What?" he asks, as if I told him he had cancer. "Are you just sore about the Bethany thing?"

"Well, I didn't love the Bethany thing, for sure," I say, "but what I realized was that I don't love you. I'm sorry, but I don't."

He snaps the box shut with an edge of anger.

"This is a surprise, Darby, after you pretty much begged me to marry you two weeks ago."

Low, I think, very low. But I let it go because it's true.

"Yes, please forgive me," I say. "I needed these two weeks to clear my head about what I really want." I don't say that I'm a completely different person now that I've had *Happy School.*

He looks at me one last time to be sure I'm in my right mind and that I'm sincere. He sees that I am, so he turns around and gets ready to drive off.

I open the passenger door and start to get out. "I'm sorry, Leland," I say.

"I understand you need some time and you've been hurt. I'll call you tomorrow," he says. "You don't mean what you're saying."

The arrogance is still thick in the air.

"It won't be different tomorrow, Leland. I've moved on," I say. Shutting the door to Leland's car, I do realize one thing, and it's that Leland and I are over forever.

As I watch Leland drive off, I notice that I feel the same emotion as when I watch the Amazon Prime driver leave the property—that is, nothing.

Peter must have been watching because he comes outside to talk to me.

"You seemed surprised to see him," Peter begins.

"I'll say," I respond, stopping to turn around. "He proposed," I say, still not believing it myself. "He actually pulled out a diamond ring and proposed," I say again.

Glancing at Peter in the dark, I can see his warm yet strong eyes staring straight at me.

"It's been a long day, and I'm exhausted. Good night, Peter," I say and walk inside.

One man proposing, whom I don't love. Another man getting married, whom I do.

Wednesday, September 5, 6:30 a.m.

I guess now would be a good time to start practicing a Morning Happiness Routine (MHR) since I am certainly not happy this morning. Let's see. What do I do?

Getting out my Quartz Journal, I review notes from yesterday's lesson. Start a Gratefulness Practice, the page says. I'm supposed to start reciting items I'm grateful for before I get out of bed, but I already forgot to do that. Okay, well, I'll read the list I wrote yesterday. I add that I'm grateful for my sense of hearing, that I can read, and that I don't have cancer.

Next, I review my Genius Zone and my Current Top Life Goals. After reading this page, I feel a focus and purpose. Third, I glance at My Enjoyment Log and What I'm Looking Forward To. I have scribbled down *design* and *cooking*, but I still need to work on finding areas of enjoyment. Honestly, I can't think of much I'm looking forward to. I do remember, however, that the Genie said no one is coming to rescue me and force me to enjoy life, so I must take responsibility to do that. I do enjoy bike rides, lying in the sun with a good book, and strolling around a farmer's market. I add those to the list.

The fourth item of an MHR, Penning Up the Farmyard Animals, is definitely needed this morning. As usual, the burden of my primary WMD, my singleness, is pressing in. I guess I could read some more books on relationships. The Genie reminded me earlier that when you study a subject in depth, the secrets rise to the top. And I certainly need all the secrets I can get if I want these old bones to find a spouse in the Peter-type category. Then, of course, I write down the burden of the loose farmyard animals, of dealing with my criminal sister and my insane mother. Yes, just as the Genie said, the carousing farmyard animals are the same today as they were yesterday.

Now for my inspirational reading. I think I'll read Charles Spurgeon's *Beside Still Waters*. Classics are always good choices. I'm glad I went to my apartment and retrieved this box of books.

Okay, I bathed my mind with the Morning Happiness Routine, and I admit that it helped. It helped a lot. Indeed, the MHR gave my mindset a different attitude and focus. (I'm pretty sure my morning coffee didn't hurt either.)

Still Wednesday, September 5, 10:00 a.m.

When I get downstairs, Peter is in the kitchen eating leftovers for breakfast.

He looks up but doesn't say anything.

"Good morning," I say, moving slowly to the fridge. "Any more leftovers?"

"I left you some," he says. "I know you like them as much as I do."

Even though Peter and I have only been sharing morning leftovers for a few days, it seems like months. There's another Peter thought. Hot Potatoes!

After microwaving the rest of the leftovers, I sit down by him at the kitchen bar.

Peter doesn't waste any time addressing the elephant in the room. "Does the fact that you don't want to work with me anymore have anything to do with Leland?" he asks.

Turning to him, I scrunch up my face. "Leland? Heavens no!"

"Not that I deserve an explanation," he says, "but I would really like one. I mean, we do amazingly together, and in a lot of ways, not just doing houses."

There he goes again. Should I tell him? I mean, he shouldn't be this nice to me or to any other girls since he's engaged.

I've got to get away and think about what to say to him. Surely I can come up with some excuse without revealing my undying love for him. Jumping up, I say, "I've got errands to run, but I still have to finish picking out a paint color for the laundry room, so I'll just meet you at the house in an hour."

He doesn't say a thing, so I grab my purse and walk out the back door.

I decide to drive to a local park. Noticing some moms and their toddlers playing nearby, I hold a guard at the door of my mind and refuse to let in the WMDs of singleness and childlessness. I park, get out of the car, and start walking. The fresh air, exercise, and scenery are already helping to clear my mind.

Hearing a text message, I glance at my phone. Maggie has texted me a picture of a huge bouquet of red roses. I see the corner of Peter's T-shirt in the photo, so I know he's also in the kitchen.

I text back. "Can you open the card and take a picture of it, please?"

Of course, I already know who sent the flowers.

Another text appears with a picture of a card with a handwritten note that says, "Darby, Please forgive me. I was an idiot. Can we please have dinner tonight? I love you, Leland."

Before I can reply to Maggie, the Genie arrives in his usual garb, but instead of sandals, he is wearing walking shoes.

"No one but you can hear or see me, Young Darby. I'm leaving for good today, and I want to say goodbye."

"Genie, I barely know the ten principles of *Happy School*," I begin to plead. "You can't leave yet. I need more instruction."

He smiles, and his kind eyes glisten.

With the absurdity of Leland's proposal, the sadness over quitting my job with Peter, and now the insecurity of losing the Genie's wisdom, I want to break down and cry.

He hands me a couple pieces of some Babylonian parchment.

"What's this?" I ask.

"These are the major principles I have taught you.[90] You must read and review them until they are your default mode for thinking."

I'll be middle-aged before they are my default thinking.

"Remember, you have merely learned the *basics* of *Happy School*," he says. "It is like you're learning to type and have merely learned where the home keys are. Now you must practice to achieve mastery. The best way to learn anything is to teach it, so find someone else who struggles with discouragement, meet with her for ten to twelve sessions, and walk through these lessons as I have walked through them with you."

With the Genie saying goodbye, I start to feel alone and afraid. But I remember that emotions come from thoughts, and I can choose an interpretation for every situation. Instead of falling into fear and self-pity that the Genie is leaving, I must focus on being grateful for all he's taught me.

"You have everything you need," he reminds me. "Everything."[91]

My throat feels thick, and I'm having trouble holding back the tears.

"The Creator's method for rebuilding a life is to rebuild the mind,"[92] he says. "You can become a completely different person if you choose to

---

90. The summaries of all the Genie's teachings in *Happy School* are at the back of this book.
91. "His divine power has granted to us all things that pertain to life and godliness" (2 Peter 1:3 NKJV).
92. "Be transformed by the renewing of your mind" (Romans 12:2 NKJV).

rebuild your mind. You are the emperor and ruler of your mind. Therefore, be exceedingly intentional about what you think."[93]

The idea that I can rebuild my life by rebuilding my mind delights me. I'm not left adrift in an ocean storm. I have a strategy.[94]

"Remember, this is a five-year program, Young Darby. In five years, you will not even recognize your former self since you will be an extremely happy, optimistic person." His smile warms me, and I want to hug him. But before I can, he begins to spin and disintegrate right before my eyes. Forever. I know I'll never see him again.

Walking back to my car, I allow myself to cry. It's fine to grieve. Humans get to grieve. I can't Move into Another Room all the time.

Still Wednesday, September 5, 11:00 a.m.

When I get to the house, Peter's truck is already there. Walking inside the house, I notice the place is dead silent.

"Peter?" I say loudly.

"I'm on the patio," he calls back.

I find him in a chair on the patio with his feet propped up on a nearby pile of lumber. He's not reading anything but simply staring into the backyard.

"What are you doing out here?" I ask.

"Thinking," he says.

"That's a good thing to do," I say, as he invites me with a motion to sit down. We both sit silently for a minute before anyone speaks.

"So Leland proposed?" he asks, turning to look at me.

"Yes," I say.

He waits. There's quite a bit of silence again before anyone speaks. Then I speak.

---

93. "Gird up the loins of your mind" (1 Peter 1:13 NKJV).
94. Reading and meditating on God's Word rebuilds the mind.

"If Leland had proposed two weeks ago, I would have said yes, and I would have been engaged to marry someone I didn't love and would have been with him for the rest of my life." I shake my head and continue. "I feel like I'm a completely different person from two weeks ago."

"So you said no to him?" Peter asks.

Surprised at the question, I say, "Of course I said no. I've told you, I don't love him. Now I feel like I have escaped from some cage or trap."

I still hate the idea that I'm almost thirty-three and single, but I do know I'll never go back to who I was with all that self-pity and dis-couragement.

As I look at Peter, I study his face one more time—his thick eye-brows, his smooth tan skin, his strong jaw. I decide that I will not give up until I find another Peter. There has to be another Peter somewhere on the planet, right?

"So when he proposed, you really told him no?" he asks again, still astonished.

"Exactly," I said. "I told him I realized I didn't love him."

He crosses his arms and looks down. Then he looks up at me again. "Okay, let me ask you one more time," he says. "And this time, please explain. Why are you not going to work with me anymore? Please, it's important that I know."

His eyes are almost begging. What's the big deal? Okay, well, I'll sort of tell him, not the whole truth, of course, but enough so he can see his inappropriate way of handling women.

"Okay, Peter I'm going to be honest. What is hard for me is that you are so nice to me, paying off my bills, buying me a lilac bush. You are funny and charming and caring. That's the problem. I can't be around this anymore." I said more than I planned to say, but what does it matter? He needs to know how women are seduced by his charms.

"Wait a minute," he says. "Can you explain to me why you can't be around someone who is nice to you? Who is interested in you?" I look at him. He is serious. He really doesn't know. Men! Are they truly this dense?

"I want to move on," I say, not wanting to explain further. "It's just best to part now before you get married in six weeks."

His eyes don't' move from mine. "What are you talking about?" he asks.

This is pretty stupid. I'm not sure what's going on. He looks rather innocent.

"You're marrying Cassie in six weeks, remember?" I'm not believing this conversation.

He leans forward in his chair with his forearms on his thighs. "Darby, Cassie is not my *fiancée;* Cassie is my *sister. Cassie* is getting married in six weeks, not me. I'm just giving her away since my father is deceased."

Thoughts are running through my mind at the speed of light. Is this possible? Could I really be this mixed up? Is it possible that maybe Maggie is so generous to Cassie because she is her actual niece? And maybe that is why Peter and Cassie don't spend more time together? And why he is annoyed out of his mind with her? Everything starts clicking.

I'm in a semi-state of shock and can't move. I can hardly breathe. They are preparing for Cassie's wedding, not Peter's.

Still, without moving or changing expression, he asks, "You thought I was marrying Cassie?"

"I did." Somehow I get that out.

Still not moving, he keeps his eyes glued to mine. "This might explain why you keep pulling away from me."

"Yes," I quietly say. I'm trying to hold in the waterworks.

Peter takes my hand. "Ever since I met you at the Vesta Home Show ten days ago, I can't get you out of my mind. And every time we work on the house, I think about us possibly living here together someday."

As much as I try to command myself, a big tear starts to roll down my cheek. This means that all of Peter's sweetness toward me was sincere. He really was interested in me and still is.

But he's not through. "I don't ever remember meeting anyone and immediately feeling like I could spend the rest of my life with them. But I felt that way about you as soon as we met."

Now the tears are escaping with more force.

He keeps talking and intertwines his fingers with mine. "I tried to explain to Aunt Maggie how you are not responsive to me. She told me to just keep trying because she thinks we are—in her words—perfect for each other."

"Maggie?" I ask. "You've talked to Maggie about me?"

"The day after I met you. She told me to go slowly, though, because you have been through a lot. Aunt Maggie keeps telling me not to give up on you."

I don't think there will ever be a bigger moment in my entire life than this one. I mean, between all the Genie's lessons in the last two weeks and now hearing this from Peter, I feel like I'm suspended in air. Not only do I have the secrets to know how to think and have a happy heart, but Peter Needleman is saying (well, almost saying) that he loves me.

Right in the middle of the stacks of tile, the piles of lumber, the marble slabs, and the electric sander, Peter takes my hand and pulls me to my feet. Very slowly and tenderly, he kisses me.

"I've been looking for you for fifteen years," he says. "And I knew it as soon as I found you."

I am tempted to tell him how broken I am, how my family is beyond dysfunctional, and how he's making a terrible mistake. But then I realize I actually have the tools to heal. I now have the tools to think, to set good goals, to make a contribution, and to be a helpful and loving person. I know I'm broken, but maybe I'm on a different path now. Maybe I could be a good wife someday and make Peter happy.

He kisses me again. When I thought before about kissing Peter, I knew it would be just like this.

If I had not met the Genie, I think I would have let my negative thinking affect my relationship with Peter. But immediately after I met the Genie and started incorporating the lessons, I changed so much. I'll never go back to letting my mind soak continually in What's Missing and Disappointing. I will now take control of my mind for the rest of my life.

I'm so happy. I am really, really happy. Thank you, Genie. Thank you with my whole heart.

Epilogue

Cassie got married as planned. She relented on insisting that Peter learn the off-the-wall dance, and Peter reluctantly agreed to wear tails. Three months later, Peter and Darby got engaged. They were engaged for six months, and then they, too, had their wedding reception at Maggie's. Darby's mother took a giant step backward after Darby started going the second mile (though not the third). Darby forgave Bailey for stealing Nana's earrings.

Darby still visits Nana on Saturday mornings.

Peter and Darby are currently renovating their third house together, and Darby is still cooking for Maggie. After the wedding, they moved into the house on Peabody. In the evenings, they enjoy each other's company on the screened-in balcony porch. Darby and Peter have a baby girl named Maggie, and Darby is pregnant with their second baby, a boy, with hopes of having two more babies in the near future.

Although Darby now has her beautiful house, a loving husband, and a precious baby, she says that her true happiness is found in *her ability to choose her thoughts.*[95]

---

95. "Whatsoever is true, whatever is noble, whatever is right, whatever is pure, whatever is lovely, whatever is admirable—if anything is excellent or praiseworthy—think about such things" (Philippians 4:8 NIV).

Information about
Happy School Study Guide

You can greatly accelerate learning the principles in *Happy School* if you also complete the 9 week study in the *Happy School Study Guide*. Text a few friends or your small group at church and spend 9 weeks changing your mindset forever.

Review and Summary of the Genie's Teaching in *Happy School*

If you review and practice the following principles for five years, you will completely transform the mental landscape of your mind.

Introduction
The Genie Arrives

1. The art and science of happiness are not new. Philosophers and theologians have studied happiness for centuries. In addition, psychologists and social scientists are now studying and documenting the subject with objective data. Happiness is actually a learnable skill.

2. There are specific thought processes and actions that chronically disappoint and discourage people repeatedly. Likewise, there is a habitual way of thinking and acting that positive, optimistic, and happy people engage in. The path has been discovered, documented, and mapped.

3. Like learning to play the piano or chess, you can learn the basics to healthy thought processes in two weeks. But it will take months or years to acquire mastery. If you follow the Genie's instructions, you will not even recognize your mental landscape in five years.

4. You can learn to think correctly about the obstacles in your life as well as think correctly about what's missing and disappointing. You do not need to *invent* rules for thinking about your problems; you only need to *discover* them.

5. Circumstances only minimally determine your happiness; it's your thinking patterns that overwhelmingly determine your happiness.

6. People learn how to think differently all the time by renewing their minds.[96] The mind is plastic, which means it can change. You now

---

96. God's plan for rebuilding a life is rebuilding the mind (Romans 12:1–2).

have many deeply carved neural pathways in your brain, much like schoolyard paths. But just as if another new schoolyard path is opened and repeatedly walked on (and the first path is no longer walked on), the second path becomes stronger and more defined while the first path gets weaker. Your neural pathways are similar. In *Happy School*, you learn to extinguish thought and behavior patterns that cause discouragement and add new thought and behavior patterns that produce joy.

7. Optimistic and pessimistic personalities can be placed on a bell curve. Although you may not ever become the most rosy, optimistic person in the world, you can radically, magnificently, and monumentally change the landscape of your brain and become a reliably positive and happy person.

8. Again, I would like to repeat this important warning: Darby is severely discouraged, even depressed. But she is not suicidal. If you have thoughts of suicide, you must tell someone who can help, such as a counselor or a pastor. *Happy School* can greatly help you with your thinking and your depression, but you may need support and intervention in the meantime until you can learn and practice all the tenets. Do not yield to despair. Things can change dramatically. Reach out to someone right this minute if you are suicidal.

Lesson 1
Thinking Determines Emotions and The Magic of Moving into Another Room in Your Brain

1. All your *emotions* are produced from your prior *thoughts*. If you are feeling sad, it is because you just experienced a sad thought. If you are scared, it is because you just experienced a fearful thought. This is always true.

2. Because your emotions come from prior thoughts, you are therefore not the *victim* of your emotions but the *producer* of them. You have been producing your emotional climate by your own thoughts. You master your moods by mastering your thoughts.

3. When the Creator made the human mind, He made it so it can only think *one thought* at a time.

4. The human brain has the phenomenal ability to "think about its own thinking." The scientific word for this is *metacognition*. Humans can stand back from their thoughts and listen in on their own self-talk. You have the power to watch the Parade of thoughts that March across Your Brain.

5. Not only can humans listen in on their self-talk, but they can also *interrupt* those thoughts (Play Hot Potatoes). They can choose to stop thinking the current thought by intentionally thinking about something else. In *Happy School*, we call this Moving into Another Room in Your Brain, and it is one of the most life-changing skills you will ever learn. It can be as simple as thinking about making a grocery list or thinking about something as profound as what you are grateful for. But because you can only think one thought at a time, you can no longer think about the original negative thought.

6. Since feelings follow thoughts, when you change your thoughts, your feelings will follow. This is marvelous to learn. You will discover that you have the *power to cast off negative thoughts and thus cast off negative emotions*. You can choose to insert (think about) whatever thoughts you choose.

7. This skill gives you power over the emotional environment in which you live since you can hear what thoughts you're thinking (the Parade Marching Across), interrupt negative thoughts (Play Hot Potatoes), and insert other thoughts instead (by Moving into Another Room in Your Brain).

8. Your discouragement and heavy heart are from thinking negative thoughts, and you have the power to exchange these thoughts for optimistic and hopeful—or even neutral—thoughts.

9. Thoughts are actual "things" that cause chemical reactions in your body. For example, when you feel fear, your heart rate increases. Thinking and ruminating on negative thoughts cause a chemical imbalance in your brain. But when you learn to think positive, hopeful, and true thoughts, your chemical imbalance begins to heal.

10. The teaching in *Happy School* is ancient thinking. These principles are how the Creator designed humans to think—to rejoice, have courage, feel blessed, have hope, learn trust, walk by faith, and find opportunity in obstacles and trials. The ten principles are all timeless.

11. Negative emotions are the warning lights on your car's dashboard, alerting you to pay attention to your prior thoughts.

Lesson 2
Quarantining What's Missing and Disappointing (the WMDs) and Reframing, Refuting, and Replacing the WMDs

1. In life there are many circumstances or situations in which one feels something or someone is missing or disappointing. In *Happy School*, these circumstances are called the WMDs, What's Missing and Disappointing. And since thoughts produce emotions, one will be emotionally down if they repeatedly ruminate about their WMDs.

2. Quarantine your WMDs. Think about them by appointment only and in only one of the following three situations: when you are researching solutions, when you are talking to someone who might have answers or solutions, and when you are in prayer.

3. Title a page in your Quartz Journal *Reframing, Refuting, or Replacing WMDs*. On the left, list your major WMDs. In the middle, write down steps of action you could take to problem-solve. On the right, reframe, refute, and replace your negative self-talk.

4. Humans tell themselves, "This obstacle is too big. This trial is insurmountable." In contrast, you must tell yourself that opportunity often shows up in the darkest places, and instead, you should expect favor to break through. Refuse to believe there is no hope. Opportunities are often hidden in seemingly unfortunate circumstances and impossibilities.

5. Don't awfulize or catastrophize your circumstances. Remind yourself that situations are *unwanted* and *not preferred,* but not cataclysmic.

Lesson 3
Don't Assign Negative Interpretations
to External Circumstances

1. Life is *as you assign it.* This fact seems counterintuitive, but it's true. Events and situations are only upsetting if you construe them to be. That is because whether you are aware of it or not, you are the one assigning an interpretation to every situation and circumstance.

2. Your happiness is relative to a scale *you've* created. Your happiness does not depend on what happens to you as much as on what conclusions you draw when events occur. External circumstances only predict a tiny portion of your happiness. People with the exact same external circumstances assign different interpretations and thus feel vastly different. You have the power to assign value to situations— that is, to write your own interpretations.

3. For most people, it is surprising to learn that they can choose a more positive and optimistic interpretation of their circumstances. It is of utmost importance that you carefully assign positive interpretations to every event and situation.

4. You can choose to view adversity as possibly laden with opportunities. You can retrain yourself to think like this, to scan for the positive and insist there are opportunities and benefits buried within the obstacle.

5. When faced with adversity, interrupt and refute your self-talk of self-pity, hopelessness, powerlessness, and coming devastation. Instead, command yourself to hope for and expect a glad surprise around the bend of the river. When you are tempted to think gloom and doom, Play Hot Potatoes, and choose to Move into Another Room. Choose courage, not self-pity. Often there are jewels hidden in adversity that were not otherwise available.

6. You can believe the obstacle is too big, or you can believe the Creator hears, cares, and is able. Dismantle your current belief system of hopelessness because the Creator is able to do immeasurably more than all you can think or imagine.

7. You can't predict happiness by a person's life events but rather by their beliefs about the events. That is because when the same event happens to different people, they draw very different conclusions about the event. People with the exact same life events end up with very different levels of life satisfaction. It's a matter of how they interpret events—how they talk to themselves.

8. Psychological stress comes from a negative perception of events. You can learn to assign a more optimistic value to every situation in your life.

9. Emotions are produced in your mind by your thoughts about your circumstances, not by the actual circumstances.

10. Your emotions don't reveal the quality of your life; they reveal the interpretation you give your circumstances. Disappointment is inevitable in life, but discouragement is optional because you get to assign an interpretation to every event and situation.

Lesson 4
The Urgent Necessity of
Stopping Bad Habits
(and How to Do It)

1. Bad habits are indulged in because of one of two—and only two—reasons: for pleasure or for dialing down emotional disturbance.

2. In a way, bad habits *are* a solution since they actually offer an effective mechanism to immediately relax the brain, soften life from the unwanted, and fill a void.

3. Bad habits are actually a con job since they only *temporarily* mask pain and in their wake leave *more* angst and pain. Bad habits lie since they promise pleasure without any negative consequences attached.

4. Your bad habits are only a temporary solution to escape and numb unfulfilling relationships, unfulfilled dreams, unfulfilled longings, dissatisfaction, and disappointment.

5. Self-discipline leads to long-term benefits, and self-indulgence leads to long-term detriments.

6. You cannot be indulging in harmful behavior and expect to be happy. Continuing in bad habits against your own better judgment is a slam-dunk recipe for self-hate and despair.

7. The human spirit can conquer almost anything, and it can definitely conquer bad habits and addictions. You absolutely can develop self-discipline and almost become an entirely different person. It's your thinking that is the problem.

8. The struggle humans have is in their own brains. Their Lower Self *pleads* for immediate pleasure and self-soothing against the better judgment of their Higher Self, which *whispers* for long-term goals.

9. One brain lobe, which houses your Lower Self, is interested in immediate gratification. Another brain lobe, which houses your Higher

Self, is interested in your long-term goals. When they compete with each other, you have cognitive dissonance.

10. Winning the battle over your Lower Self is of utmost importance, but many people go a lifetime without this accomplishment. A victory over your Lower Self—your desire for immediate gratification—will completely change your life. Overcoming your Lower Self's schemes will catapult your sense of dignity and self-esteem. To be happy, one must remove the disagreement inside their mind and conquer their Lower Self.

11. Here are the seven steps to saying no to your Lower Self:

    a. Know and write out the Detriments of Continuing and the Benefits of Stopping your bad habit. Having powerful and compelling reasons is always the first key to changing habits. Until you strongly desire something, you will not have motivation to do something differently.

    b. Write out a proclamation of your Best Sane Higher Self. Write out what your Best Sane Higher Self wants in moments of complete sanity (versus in the undertow and ambush of your addiction.)

    c. Know the arguments your Lower Self will use to entice you to *not* follow your Best Sane Higher Self proclamation. It will always be some form of the sentence, "Wouldn't it be nice to…" and then it will begin its reasons. You can hear the reasons if you Listen to the Parade Marching across Your Brain. Your Lower Self will try to persuade you that you can have self-indulgence without any price or consequences. Your Lower Self does not want to be instructed by your Higher Self.

    d. Be ready to talk back to your Lower Self with your Best Sane Higher Self proclamation. The key is that you remind your Lower Self that your Higher Self, *the judge and jury,* has surveyed all the evidence carefully when you were in your best sane mind (not now in the undertow of sabotage, ambush, and craving). The verdict of your Best Sane Higher Self is that you must abstain for your ultimate happiness and well-being. Say to your Lower Self, "I hear you ranting and raving, but you do not have my best interests at heart. In the morning—my times of peak clarity—my Best Sane Higher Self knows that this bad habit is not good for me." You've heard all the reasons your Lower Self uses, and you've refuted them. There are no good reasons left. None. So there is really nothing to discuss with your Lower Self. This battle is fought and won in your mind. You do not have to give in to a craving. Cravings are urges, not commands, even though their intensity may feel like a command.

e. Be smoke, and let the dart of the craving pass through.

f. Immediately Move into Another Room in Your Brain.

g. Decide what you will do instead to self-soothe and entertain. Write out a list in your Quartz Journal: *Alternatives I Will Choose for Comfort and Entertainment.*

12. If your Lower Self is able to seduce you or ambush you, that doesn't mean the seven-step plan doesn't work. It only means the Lower Self *had a reason that you weren't prepared for.* Listen closely to the reason your Lower Self gives you that extends permission for you to indulge. Write that scheme in your Quartz Journal, and refute it. Your Lower Self only has about twenty—not 2,000—reasons why it's permissible to indulge. The road to conquering a bad habit is fourfold: try, fail, analyze what went wrong, and try again. You must write down your Lower Self's schemes because the brain will not recall them under the siege of a craving.

13. The grooves in your brain that remember your bad habit will never completely go away. Even if you've defeated your bad habit for a year or more, suddenly the cravings can re-appear. But Listen to the Parade Marching across Your Brain. Your Lower Self will still be using some version of "Wouldn't it be nice to…" followed by a reason such as "I'm sure I can handle (my bad habit) now."

14. People stop doing bad habits instantly all the time as their brain suddenly realizes that the detriments they are incurring are ludicrous to continue. They see the battle between their Lower Self and their

Higher Self plainly and can now choose. It's almost as if a veil is pulled back, and the bad habit and its cravings are immediately met with disapproval or disgust.

15. If you can convince your Higher Self that you don't want your bad habit (because of the many detriments), you can easily and peacefully end the struggle of your brain with this seven-step method.

16. You don't have to deal with your inner childhood demons to stop a bad habit. You stop because of the detriments and benefits. Only after stopping will you be *clear* so you can then deal with your family-of-origin issues. Stop first. All you need in order to stop is to plainly, clearly, and loudly (as through a megaphone) *hear the reasons*. Reasons. Reasons. They will bathe your mind and give you the power to quietly choose against your Lower Self that continually pleads for pleasure yet harms you.

17. Confront the lie that life has few other pleasures so you need your bad habit. There's the pleasure of reading, the pleasure of seeing, the pleasure of hearing, the joy of learning, the joy of stimulating conversation, the joy of nature, the joy of hobbies, the joy of laughter, and the joy of using your gifts. There is *untold* joy and pleasure to be found without negative detriments attached.

18. Another lie to be confronted is that life and fulfillment are found in pleasure, status, power, ease, enjoying your sexual preferences, and no responsibility. The truth is that true satisfaction is tethered to self-discipline, which is needed to build a life with contribution (Lesson 5), deep relationships (Lesson 9), and virtue (discussed in *Happy School Advanced*).

19. Life has hardship, loneliness, hard knocks, and difficulties. Your choice to respond to those unwanted scenarios is either self-indulgence or self-discipline. You must quarantine your disappointment while you work to solve your problems. Your Higher Self now knows how to quarantine unpleasantness and how to Move into Another Room in Your Brain. You do not need negative fillers to handle life.

20. No discovery will ever eclipse the importance of human beings developing self-discipline. Self-control has always been and will always be one of the major secrets to happiness and satisfaction.

21. It is actually not that hard to avoid the thing that is harming your life. In light of that truth, it's not a big deal to quit your bad habit. The trick to stopping bad habits is to see the reality of the harm. Bad habits are *not* insurmountable impediments.

Lesson 5
Discover Your One-of-a-Kind Genius Zone and Set Your Current Top Life Goals

1. By discovering the three-way intersection of your *skills*, your *interests*, and a worthwhile *need*, you can determine your Genius Zone.

2. There is error in thinking that a life of ease and constant pleasure is what makes humans happy. In stark contrast, theologians and philosophers have known for centuries that a life with deep, true payoffs is *not* one of pursuing constant ease and pleasure. Instead, making a meaningful contribution with one's skill and interest set is one of the greatest endeavors that will satisfy the human soul. Loving excessive ease, entertainment, and idleness is a sure-fire recipe for eventual despair. Leisure is a *reward* for work, not an end in itself. Excessive leisure strips one of their own self-respect.

3. Not only is it the *duty* of humans to be beneficial to their fellow human beings with their skills and interest sets, but it is *a secret* of their happiness.

4. Dedication to a worthy purpose engages the mind and brings satisfaction. It feels invigorating to work hard at goals you care about. Having an aim outside of yourself gives the mind purpose, freeing it from the dark despair of self-absorption.

5. One sign that you are living below your potential is chronic boredom. You will be unhappy if you are less that you're capable of. A dull life that is void of color and zest reveals that a person is living below their capability. If you play it safe and avoid being all you can be, you are asking for despair. You must become alive to your potential and discover inspiring work.

6. Thinking about expressing your Genius Zone is actually a fabulous antidote to feeling crushed and weighed down. Thinking about your Genius Zone is one of the best Rooms for Your Brain to Move Into, away from your WMDs. The world needs your Genius Zone. It is a healing

modality for your chronic boredom, dissatisfaction, and self-loathing. People know they are chronically bored, but fear keeps them in the stands and out of the arena where true living takes place. Humans must throw their hearts over the fence, and their bodies will follow.

7. At the top of a page in your Quartz Journal, write *Discover Your One-of-a-Kind Genius Zone*. Divide the page into three columns. On the left, list all the *skills* you can think of that you possess. In the center, list all your *interests.* Later you can address the right column, which are ideas on how you might use your Genius Zone to contribute to society.

8. As you know, if you are not in the right field or job, it is comparable to pushing a cart uphill all day.

9. After you discover and pinpoint your Genius Zone, immerse yourself in it. Create a life of being useful with your gifts. Discover where a deep gladness meets a need. There's true joy in offering what you sense you were made to give.

10. You have a duty to use your skills and interests to repair this world's broken ruins. Much human flourishment lies on the other side of using your talents and interests to achieve worthwhile goals.

11. Create a page in your Quartz Journal called *Current Top Life Goals.* As all life coaches know, you must begin with the end in mind. So write down goals for the next ten or twenty years. You begin with the end in mind and work backward. What is the outcome you want? Make a *plan* to get there.

12. The secret to *achieving* goals is to formulate a specific plan and then work the plan. A dream is only a dream until you devise a plan.

13. Having compelling and exciting goals is imperative to humans. We are aiming creatures, and without goals, humans eventually disintegrate emotionally. It is satisfying and fulfilling to reach for mastery in an area. Challenge yourself to reach beyond mediocre with your Genius Zone since there's joy to be found in mastery. Become phenomenally competent in your chosen area. Don't do average work; do killer work.

14. Know that the way to conquer huge goals is exactly the same as eating an elephant—one bite at a time. Daily plow and grind on your goals. Lay bricks every day, and soon you will have built a cathedral. Hudson Taylor described three stages to every project: Impossible. Difficult. Done.

15. There is too much talk about people being brilliant. However, what is rare and breathtaking is a person who has serious goals and uses discipline to hammer away at their goals.

16. You will face unwanted tasks when you are trying to reach goals. Those unpleasant but necessary tasks are called *frogs*, and you must eat your frogs every day. Do the difficult or unpleasant tasks (eat your frogs) early in the day when your Willpower Points are still high (you only have a certain number of Willpower Points allotted for each day). Your brain will say to you, "I'd rather not do that unpleasant or difficult task." But you have to find a way to make yourself eat your frogs every day. Successful people make themselves do hard things.

17. Knowing you only have so many Willpower Points available each day is helpful since it helps you realize that it is probably best to get high priority items and difficult jobs done early in the day.

18. Quit playing small and safe, and instead, take calculated risks. Yes, you will be criticized, and you must brace yourself for that. No one likes criticism, but no one ever did anything of substance without being criticized. Don't let the naysayers get you down.

19. Develop some guts, some bravery, and a thick skin by choosing your thoughts carefully. This is the only path to create a life you're proud of. No one is proud of a small, fearful, mediocre life. No one is proud of hunkering down with a mood changer to escape the pressure of doing something important and noble.

20. Some people naturally know how to set and achieve goals. But setting and achieving goals is a learnable skill, even if it's not easy or natural.

Lesson 6
Rooms to Stay Out Of:
Self-Pity, Failure, and Regret

1. Self-pity is feeling sorry for yourself because you don't have more of something. Self-pity can come from not having certain physical attributes or from feeling you did not receive enough natural talents, gifts, attention, or even respect. Self-pity can come from thinking that you have not had the same opportunities or advantages that others have had, or from feeling violated or harmed by others. Self-pity can come from feeling trapped in a situation or from not having something specific you truly desire. Self-pity can also arise when you don't feel you have received enough attention or appreciation from others. The sources of self-pity are infinite, but in every case, self-pity means you feel sorry for yourself in an area because you don't have enough of something you desire.

2. Individuals with the exact same objective situation or circumstance often give their circumstances completely different interpretations (see Lesson 3). For example, one person feels victimized by fate and carries a sense of being injured (thus feeling sorry for themselves), while another person—remember, one with the exact same circumstance—does not feel sorry for themselves. The difference is that humans assign value to and interpret all situations and circumstances.

3. Having a victim mentality and self-pity is one of the greatest weaknesses of the human spirit. It is really nothing less than denying the responsibility you've been given. Self-pity is acid to the human soul.

4. Of course, you didn't script certain situations, but they are here. Now the question is, what interpretation are you going to give them?

5. You can feel sorry for yourself and whine and complain about how hard and unfair life is. Or you can choose to be one of the rare, the magnificent, and the noble, who takes charge of their thoughts and refuses to have self-pity. These people take their unwanted situation

and apply a better interpretation to it. They insist in their mind that other people's inconsideration and harm (as well as other difficult situations) will be a springboard from which they return good for evil or a blessing for insult. These are the mature in life, believing there's opportunity in obstacles. Noble people have powerful and inspiring goals and press toward them in spite of obstacles and difficulties.

6. Maybe in your opinion you've been dealt some difficult circum-stances, but ruminating about how hard your circumstances are is a completely monumental waste of energy and time. Problem-solve or quarantine!

7. As you now realize, you get to choose what mental landscape you are going to live in by constantly monitoring the Parade that Marches across Your Brain, interrupting your self-talk, quarantining your negative thoughts, and reframing, refuting, or replacing your nega-tivity by telling yourself another story. Then choose more profitable thoughts (Move into Another Room). You are in charge of your thoughts, and that includes giving an interpretation to everything that happens to you.

8. There is no time for self-pity if you are focusing on mastery of your Genius Zone and goals.

9. People claim self-pity so others will feel sympathy for them. But in stark contrast, it actually causes others to lose respect for them.

10. Humans' pasts often include many mistakes, foolish behaviors, and other self-defeating behaviors. You must forgive yourself for your past shortcomings. Will yourself to see your past failures as an oppor-tunity to learn and grow. Realize that great suffering often leads to great positive change.

11. Reason aggressively with your voice of inadequacy, and turn off your inner critic. It is a total waste of time to wish for a different set of circumstances or to play a Failure Movie from the past in your mind.

12. If you read or listen to biographies of great men and women, they invariably point to their failures as the springboard to their success.

This is about your mind. This is about guarding your mind's thoughts, insisting that you use your past failures merely as feedback.

13. Yes, of course you have some past failures, but learn from them, gather your strength, and strike out again. Refuse to let the failures define you. Humans rise from abysmal failures all the time.

14. After you have dissected your failures for possible wisdom or learning, draw a line in the sand, and quarantine the event, guarding your mind from your negative self-critic.

15. Think of your brain as the landlord of a large apartment complex. You decide what tenants live there. Do you allow the tenants (thoughts of self-pity and failure or regret) to overrun your property, or do you purposely attract desirable tenants to live there? You choose what to do with your thoughts. You are the landlord of your mind.

Lesson 7
More Rooms to Stay Out Of:
Being Offended, Angry, and Resentful

1. If humans begin to pay attention, they will realize how often they get offended. Their family, co-workers, bosses, employees, friends, and even store clerks frequently offend them.

2. A helpful strategy to embrace when offended is to see the offense as a dart coming toward you, but you do *not* let the offense land. In other words, be like smoke, and let the dart of the offense pass through you.

3. In large offenses, you have to go beyond not being offended. You have to *forgive*. Forgiving and not being offended are, however, definitely close cousins.

4. You do not have to continue to be in a close relationship with toxic people, but on your part—*your part*—it is imperative that you forgive, that you "empty their boxes of offenses" because harboring anger and hate toward others tarnishes *your* soul. The human body was not built to carry anger, resentment, and hate. In fact, science is now revealing that physical harm is done to a person's health when they regularly experience anger, hate, and resentment. Remember how the thought of fear increases your physical heart rate? Thoughts are things and do have a physical effect on your body. You must learn to not be offended and to forgive since your very health is at stake. People's health often improves when they learn to overlook offenses and forgive.

5. When a thought comes to mind that you are offended or that you harbor resentment, you choose right there what to do with the thought. You practice! You practice this skill of overlooking offenses and forgiving others as you would practice any skill. You will learn to be proficient in time. Being offended and resentful are the default modes that are now written in the hardware of your mind. But with

practice and repetition, you can learn to more easily overlook and forgive.

6. Few lessons in life will do more for your relationships as well as your emotional health as learning to overlook offenses and forgive others. It is extremely high human functioning. Be smoke when you're offended, and empty their boxes of offenses when you are mistreated. Refuse to cling to any hard feelings against anyone. Be a perpetual forgiveness machine.

7. Anger stems from pride. Anger appears when one is upset over having blocked goals. Humility and meekness are the antidotes.

Lesson 8
More Rooms to Stay Out Of:
Worry and Fear

1. Humans vary greatly in their tendency to worry. The optimists in life get fired but are excited about the opportunity to start anew. Pessimists, on the other hand, are certain that a headache is a brain tumor.

2. Not all worry and fear are bad. People need to be afraid of danger such as fire. But humans often excessively worry about relationships, money, health, and any number of topics.

3. People see their external circumstances as the *cause* of their anxiety, but they are not. Worry is caused by worrying *thoughts*.

4. Worry happens when the mind projects itself into the future and imagines something going wrong. Worry often amplifies a situation and turns it into a catastrophe.

5. When you worry excessively, it is as if your thoughts are stuck running through an endless repeat cycle. But you can *interrupt* those anxious thoughts and break the loop. You can quarantine thoughts that make you worry and think about them only during one of the three problem-solving times that are repeatedly referred to. Play Hot Potatoes. Be smoke, and let the worry pass through you. Then Move into Another Room in your Brain, and think about something else. Your greatest weapon against worry is your ability to think another thought.

6. Determine if your worry is solvable. If it is, brainstorm solutions in your Quartz Journal. Research, analyze, plan, and take action to solve your problems. But at the end of that session, you must quarantine your thoughts again.

7. If your worry is not solvable, you will need to work on the principle of acceptance and begin to understand and accept the uncertainty of life.

8. You are not the victim of your anxiety but the producer of it. By listening in on the Parade of Thoughts that March across Your Brain, you will be able to discern the thoughts you are having, and then you can refute, replace, or reframe them.

9. The first practical suggestion to dial down anxiety is to remember the huge ability of exercise to affect your brain chemistry. Exercise literally changes the brain because of the hormones produced when exercising. Increasing exercise is the first prescription anyone should try if they are plagued with worry or anxiety.

10. The second practical suggestion is to address your diet. Sugar and processed carbs are notoriously horrible for your emotional state, as is alcohol. Good nutrition is non-negotiable for good mental health.

11. A third suggestion that diffuses anxiety is talking to a trusted person who will listen without criticizing you.

12. The best tool for handling anxiety is prayer. Prayer and meditation actually change structures in your brain.

13. Drugs only provide short-term help. What is essential is to look at the root of your anxiety, which is your thoughts.

14. Unless you face imminent physical harm, worry and fear are just bad management of your mind.

Lesson 9
The Premiere Importance
of Relationships

1. The rules to grow great relationships are the same as they've been for 6,000 years. There are no new tricks or methods. Certain behaviors produce respectful and caring relationships, and certain behaviors repel meaningful relationships.

2. Having good relationships is the number one most important component of happiness.

3. A non-negotiable principle in having great relationships is that you must be a person others can *trust*. You can do everything else right, but if you lie, are deceitful, or don't keep your promises, others will not genuinely feel positive toward you. No one is smart enough to break this rule and get by with it indefinitely. Eventually, those without integrity in a relationship will be found out, and others will pull away emotionally from them. Therefore, be trustworthy to the maximum degree.

4. The second principle to understand about relationships is that they always have a sowing and reaping component. Examples of qualities and actions that grow relationships are giving admiration, attention, appreciation, and acceptance. In addition, performing acts of service, giving gifts, and being reliable and responsible grow good relationships. Agree wholeheartedly, but disagree softly. Be affirming, loyal, and in a good mood. Offer others compassion, kindness, and patience as well as tenderness, warmth, and mercy. Do more than your share. Qualities and actions that repel human hearts are being dishonest, critical, accusatory, negative, unkind, and argumentative. Giving too much advice and insisting on being right all the time drives others away as does being irresponsible, undependable, lazy, complaining, or selfish.

5. The third principle one must understand in order to grow meaningful relationships is that people want to be known and understood. They want you to know how they feel, what they want, and what their

dreams and calling are. They want you to discern what is important to them. Therefore, it is imperative that you learn and develop the skill of Asking World-Class Questions and Giving World-Class Listening. Asking World-Class Questions allows other people to talk about what they are interested in. You encourage others to continue talking by maintaining eye contact and continuing to ask them questions such as "What happened next?" and "Tell me more." People love to talk about their ideas, opinions, and activities, but only to interested parties. World-Class Listening includes never losing eye contact when the other person is talking. Giving World-Class Listening is a rare skill but draws the human heart like the moon draws the tides.

6. Intentionally seek to understand someone. Determine to listen twice as much as you talk.

7. The fourth principle to skyrocket the depth and satisfaction of your relationships is to make a decision to initiate for the other person's benefit. That is, decide to help those in your inner circle get what they want. *Sacrifice to help them with their happiness and goals.* Have a mindset that you give more than you take.

8. Study how to improve another person's welfare. Be that person who helps other people's lives get better by helping them with their goals and happiness. *Love is a decision to act in the best interest of another.*

9. The fifth principle to grow and deepen relationships is to know how to react when another person disappoints you. People are half-strengths and half-weaknesses. That means everyone in your inner circle will have a weakness set (such as lack of attention, lack of dependability, etc.). You must have a system to know how to think about and deal with others' weakness set instead of being massively disappointed. The secret is to learn how to forego and overlook them. Sometimes others will ignore you, keep you waiting, treat you rudely, show others preference, interrupt, criticize you, complain about you, be negative, or be annoying. But you can choose how to interpret all of those events. You can interpret them as disappointing (and awf-ulize their actions), or you can forego and overlook. You can learn to

reconstrue thoughts that seem negative. Remember, things are only a certain way if you construe them to be. Refuse to be offended, and instead continue to focus on how *you* love and give. To forgive another, you take their box of grievances and turn the box upside down, emptying the contents. You empty their accounts. Bitterness makes your soul tiny, warped, mangled, and shriveled. Nothing is worse for the human heart than bitterness. Refuse to keep any bitterness toward anyone. Forgive extravagantly. The only free person is the person who can forgive.

10. The sixth major principle is to drop the expectation that others will love and give to you in the manner you prefer. Instead, shift from focusing on who doesn't love and give to you enough to how you love and give to others. Yes, humans naturally focus on how they aren't treated right by others, aren't respected enough, honored enough, or given enough attention and praise. Get rid of the expectations that others will treat you special and that they will be grateful and appreciative. This thinking only causes self-pity.

11. The seventh principle to establishing great relationships is to develop humility. Take the blame, give the credit. Cheerfully take correction and constructive criticism. Be smoke, and try to learn from others' accusations. (Usually there is a hair of truth in most criticism.) Humans hate to admit they are wrong, but you should be quick to say, "I was wrong. Will you please forgive me?"

12. If possible, when people are repeatedly difficult and toxic and you have repeatedly tried and failed to resolve the conflict between you (for example, with a boss), it is best, if possible, to remove yourself from that environment. However, when the toxic person is a family member, you do not want estrangement. Therefore, the advice is to go the proverbial first mile. Then, as instructed in the Creator's Word, go the "second mile" with your toxic relative; that is, do *more* than what is expected. You do not have to go the *third mile*. That's where you have boundaries. This is the principle that protects you from getting sucked into a toxic person's negative world. Go the first

and second miles, but then draw a line in the sand since you don't have to go the third. You won't believe how going the second mile will calm many toxic people.

13. Difficult people are sometimes a gift in disguise since they enable you to clearly see what you *don't* want to become. Just because you grew up with a critical and negative person does not mean you are doomed to duplicate those thinking patterns. Remember, the brain is plastic and can change. You are now an adult and can choose to renew and reprogram your mind. You can break a previous, unhealthy generational cycle.

14. No one is coming on a white horse to help you form deep, meaningful relationships. And since relationships are about 70 percent of your happiness, you have to take responsibility to initiate and form them yourself. Remember, how you care for others is a measure of your true greatness.

15. Think about whether you have offended or harmed anyone else. If you have, you need to go to them, admit you were wrong, and ask their forgiveness. In many circles, this is called making amends, and it is absolutely crucial that you do so in order to get emotional freedom. Learn to apologize quickly when you err. Having a clear conscience with others is a non-negotiable principle to having a happy heart.

Lesson 10
The Importance of a
Morning Happiness Routine (MHR)

1. Some people wake up in a sunny, warm emotional climate, just like some people wake up in a sunny, warm physical climate. Knowing that you wake up in a "winter emotional environment" means you have to take proactive steps every morning to warm up your mind and perspective.

2. This daily routine is called a Morning Happiness Routine (MHR) and is of utmost importance since it will jump-start your mind to begin to think positively and correctly.

3. If you had diabetes, you would check your blood sugar every morning and eat something if it's low. You'd give yourself a shot if it's high. It you had problems with walking, you would attach a brace to your leg every morning. You personally have trouble with discouragement, and your very life's happiness is at stake. This twenty-minute Morning Happiness Routine is a small price to pay for giving yourself the advantage of a positive mindset first thing every morning.

4. The first aspect of the Morning Happiness Routine, the MHR, is creating a Gratefulness Practice. As soon as you gain consciousness in the morning, even before you get out of bed, begin listing things you're grateful for. This is a habit for you to do first thing for the rest of your life.

5. The second of the five MHR activities is to review your Genius Zone and your Current Top Life Goals. The natural mind easily forgets what its mission and vision are and therefore needs daily reminders.

6. The third list is called *My Enjoyment Log and What I'm Looking Forward To*. It is your responsibility to make time to enjoy your life, not anyone else's. Often people focus on their WMDs to such an extent that they don't take responsibility for adding activities that give them joy.

7. The fourth list is Penning Up the Farmyard Animals. The example of the wild farmyard animals is like your multiple WMDs that run amok in your mind in the morning. Therefore, write down on a page all your pressing problems each morning. What you will eventually see is that you have the same negative thoughts and problems every morning. As you continue to problem-solve and work on your problems (in one of the three times allowed), you will realize that you are making progress. Penning up the Farmyard Animals is incredibly beneficial as you get your WMDs out of your mind and onto paper where you can deal with them later. Quarantining problems by putting them in boxes with tops until a later time when you can problem-solve is one of the most valuable skills you will learn in *Happy School.*

8. The fifth and last MHR activity is to have inspirational reading ready in the morning to bathe your mind with hopeful and truthful thoughts. This may be the best log of all.

9. Having a daily Morning Happiness Routine is another great tool in your arsenal for rebuilding life-changing neural pathways.

The Genie Departs

1. Remember, you have merely been introduced to the *basics* of *Happy School*. An analogy is that you're learning to type and you've merely learned where the home keys are. Now you must practice to achieve mastery. The best way to learn anything is to teach it, so find someone else who struggles with discouragement, and meet with that person for ten to twelve sessions, walking through these lessons as the Genie walked through them with Darby.

2. The Creator's method for *rebuilding a life is to rebuild the mind*. You can become a completely different person. You are the emperor and ruler of your mind. Be exceedingly intentional about what you think about.

3. This is a five-year program. In five years, you will not even recognize your former self since you will be a happy, optimistic person.

Lists for Your Quartz Journal

List 1: Rethinking Your WMDs. Make three columns. The left column is titled WMDs, the middle column is Actions to Take, and the third column is Replace, Refute, or Replace.

List 2: Six Steps to Stopping Bad Habits

1. Write out the Detriments of Continuing and the Benefits of Stopping your bad habit.

2. Write out a proclamation of My Best Sane Higher Self.

3. Write out the arguments your Lower Self will use to entice you to *not* follow your Best Sane Higher Self proclamation.

4. Write out how you will be ready to talk back to your Lower Self with your Best Sane Higher Self proclamation.

5. Be smoke, and let the dart of the craving pass through.

6. Make a list of what topics you will think about (Rooms to Move Into) or Alternate Activities to Do instead of your bad habit when you need to self-soothe and entertain.

List 3: Discover Your One-of-a-Kind Genius Zone. Make three columns: Skills, Interests, and a Need in the World.

List 4: Begin a Morning Happiness Practice

1. Begin a Gratefulness Practice.

2. Rewrite or review your Genius Zone and your Current Top Life Goals.

3. Make a My Enjoyment Log and What I'm Looking Forward To.

4. Practice Penning Up the Farmyard Animals.

5. Do some Inspirational Reading.

Optional but recommended: A brisk walk outside.

Acknowledgments

A generous and world-class listener, my husband, David, is also dependably witty and unselfish. He is the proverbial tortoise that eventually wins every race. David's suggestions on this manuscript dramatically improved it. In fact, he dramatically improves about everything he touches.

Thank you to my early groups. It was delightful to watch you learn how to Watch the Parade, Play Hot Potatoes, and then Move into Another Room. I also loved watching you learn to be smoke when you were offended. Great work, you guys!

A fond thank you to my early readers, Kendall, Leslie, Jeanne, Sheri, Nancy, Denise, Vicki Lynn, Chelsea, and Bethany. Your comments were extremely helpful. I am blessed to know each of you.

And finally, I have a huge amount of gratitude for the thousands of authors I have read over the past forty years. My favorite delivery is still a box with new books.

About the Author

At 25 years old, Julie Gordon encountered a radical rethink about all of life. As a worldly pre-med student, she *coincidentally* was studying evolution in a biology course. After discovering that evolution was an empty theory and a merely fallacious conjecture, and reading some brilliant apologists such as C. S. Lewis and Josh McDowell (and maybe most importantly listening to preaching by Adrian Rogers), she surrendered her life to Jesus Christ.

For the next thirty years, Julie and her husband, David, raised six children. During that time, Julie's favorite things to study were relationships, health, overcoming discouragement, and, of course, the Bible.

Although Julie has a master's degree in Marriage and Family Counseling, she believes that mentoring other women and reading hours a day is what God used to bring these secrets to the surface.

Julie's favorite person and best friend is her husband, David. They enjoy walking, watching good TV series, biking, cooking, and listening to good preaching and worship. And of course, they enjoy their adult children and precious grandchildren.

With the *Genie* series now complete, Julie will turn her time and attention to writing a book for skeptics. As of this writing, she is still waiting on one gigantic prayer to be answered.

Please feel free to write Julie at JulieNGordon2012@gmail.com with any comments or suggestions. She loves getting e-mail from her readers.

This book's purpose is to teach others how to corral and cage negative thoughts and thus be happier. However, it cannot help one become *good*. Humans need God's living and active Word to change their hearts.

Sanctify them through thy truth:
thy word is truth (John 17:17 KJV).

Made in the USA
Coppell, TX
07 November 2021

65364985R00166